Praise for *Six Impossible Things*

'[A]n accessible primer on all things quantum ... rigorous and chatty.'
   Sunday Times

'Gribbin has inspired generations with his popular science writing, and this, his latest offering, is a compact and delightful summary of the main contenders for a true interpretation of quantum mechanics. ... If you've never puzzled over what our most successful scientific theory means, or even if you have and want to know what the latest thinking is, this new book will bring you up to speed faster than a collapsing wave function.'
   Jim Al-Khalili

'Gribbin gives us a feast of precision and clarity, with a phenomenal amount of information for such a compact space. It's a TARDIS of popular science books, and I loved it. ... This could well be the best piece of writing this grand master of British popular science has ever produced, condensing as it does many years of pondering the nature of quantum physics into a compact form.'
   Brian Clegg, popularscience.co.uk

'Elegant and accessible ... Highly recommended for students of the sciences and fans of science fiction, as well as for anyone who is curious to understand the strange world of quantum physics.'
   Forbes

EIGHT

IMPROBABLE

POSSIBILITIES

EIGHT

IMPROBABLE

POSSIBILITIES

The Mystery of the Moon,
and Other Implausible
Scientific Truths

JOHN

GRIBBIN

ICON

This edition published in the UK in 2023
by Icon Books Ltd, Omnibus Business Centre,
39–41 North Road, London N7 9DP
email: info@iconbooks.com
www.iconbooks.com

Previously published in the UK in 2021 by Icon Books Ltd

Sold in the UK, Europe and Asia
by Faber & Faber Ltd, Bloomsbury House,
74–77 Great Russell Street,
London WC1B 3DA or their agents

Distributed in the UK, Europe and Asia
by Grantham Book Services, Trent Road,
Grantham NG31 7XQ

Distributed in Australia and New Zealand
by Allen & Unwin Pty Ltd, PO Box 8500,
83 Alexander Street, Crows Nest, NSW 2065

Distributed in South Africa
by Jonathan Ball, Office B4, The District,
41 Sir Lowry Road, Woodstock 7925

ISBN: 978-178578-979-3

Typeset in Whitman by Marie Doherty

Printed and bound in Great Britain by
Clays Ltd, Elcograf S.p.A.

CONTENTS

John Gribbin's numerous bestselling books include *In Search of Schrödinger's Cat*, *The Universe: A Biography*, *13.8: The Quest to Find the True Age of the Universe and the Theory of Everything*, and *Out of the Shadow of a Giant: How Newton Stood on the Shoulders of Hooke and Halley*.

His most recent book is *Seven Pillars of Science: The Incredible Lightness of Ice, and Other Scientific Surprises*. His earlier title, *Six Impossible Things: The 'Quanta of Solace' and the Mysteries of the Subatomic World*, was shortlisted for the Royal Society Insight Investment Science Book Prize for 2019.

He is an Honorary Senior Research Fellow at the University of Sussex, and was described as 'one of the finest and most prolific writers of popular science around' by the *Spectator*.

For Steve Guest, who appreciates things like this!

ACKNOWLEDGEMENTS

Once again, I am grateful to the Alfred C. Munger Foundation for financial support, and to the University of Sussex for providing a base and research facilities.

As with all my books, Mary Gribbin ensured that I did not stray too far into the thickets of incomprehensibility, and on this occasion Improbability Eight owes a particular debt to her. The mistakes, of course, are all mine.

LIST OF ILLUSTRATIONS

'When you have excluded the impossible, whatever remains, however improbable, must be the truth.'

The Adventure of the Beryl Coronet,
Arthur Conan Doyle

PREFACE

What Do We Know?

S cience deals with the unknown. My non-scientist friends sometimes offer sympathy when what is perceived as the 'failure' of a scientific theory makes headline news. This happened recently with the discovery that the expansion of the Universe is speeding up, and that our simple Big Bang model needs modification. 'You must be very disappointed,' they say, 'that your beautiful theory is wrong.' Not at all! Good scientists are delighted when new evidence hints that new ideas are needed to explain what is going on in the world. New ideas are the lifeblood of science, and if all our theories were perfect descriptions of the world (by which I mean everything there is, not just planet Earth), there would be nothing left for scientists to do.

You might be surprised that there is anything much for science to do at all. Given how much we already know about how the world works, what is there left to discover? But a warning lesson from history cautions against such complacency. Towards the end of the nineteenth century, there was a widespread feeling among physicists that with Isaac Newton's theory of gravity and James Clerk Maxwell's theory of electromagnetism they had all the tools they needed to describe the world, and that no new fundamental discoveries remained to be made. In 1894 A.A. Michelson, an American physicist remembered for his work on measuring the speed of light, said:

> While it is never safe to affirm that the future of Physical Science has no marvels in store even more astonishing than those of the past, it seems probable that most of the grand underlying principles have been firmly established and that further advances are to be sought chiefly in the rigorous application of these principles to all the phenomena which come under our notice. It is here that the science of measurement shows its importance – where quantitative work is more to be desired than qualitative work. An eminent physicist remarked that the future truths of physical science are to be looked for in the sixth place of decimals.

It was just as well he put in the opening caveat, because hot on the heels of that remark came the discovery of radioactivity, the special and general theories of relativity, and quantum physics. Definitely marvels even more astonishing than those of the past. Scientists have learned never to say that all that remains is to dot the i's and cross the t's of their favoured theories.

How can there be more to be discovered when so much is already known? An analogy may help. Pretend that everything we know about the world is represented by the area inside a small circle drawn on a large, flat piece of paper. Everything we know is inside the circle, everything we don't know is outside. As we discover more about how the world works, the circle gets bigger. But as it does so, the circumference of the circle, the boundary between what we know and what we don't know, also gets bigger. As the Lovin' Spoonful song 'She is Still a Mystery' puts it, 'the more I see, the more I see there is to see'. There will be plenty of work for scientists in the foreseeable future. And that work proceeds by setting up hypotheses (or guesses) about how the world works, then carrying out experiments or making observations to eliminate the incorrect guesses.

Are relativists delighted when a new observation of the Universe confirms, as the headline writers like to put it, that 'Einstein Was Right'? Only up to a point. What would be really exciting for them would be an observation which showed that the general theory of relativity is good as far as it goes, but that it may not be right everywhere and all the time. That is why such experiments are carried out. Not to 'prove Einstein was right' but in the hope of finding out the conditions, or places, in the Universe where Einstein's theory might be wrong.

So in spite of what popular media may tell you, good scientists do not carry out experiments in order to prove their pet theory is right.* They carry out experiments in order to find

------

* There are, of course, bad scientists who do just that, but they have no place here.

where the theory fails, which tells them where new discoveries can be made (and, if you care about such things, where Nobel Prizes might be won).

As Richard Feynman famously pointed out:

> If it disagrees with experiment, it is wrong. In that simple statement is the key to science. It does not make any difference how beautiful your guess is, it does not make any difference how smart you are, who made the guess, or what his name is – if it disagrees with experiment, it is wrong.

This is the scientific equivalent of Conan Doyle's dictum. It is by experiment (or observation) that scientists eliminate the impossible. Thomas Henry Huxley called this 'The great tragedy of science – the slaying of a beautiful hypothesis by an ugly fact.'

But a good scientist doesn't go quite as far as Doyle does. Once you have eliminated the impossible, whatever is left is certainly possible, in the light of present knowledge, but may not be the ultimate truth. It may yet, in its turn, be slain by an ugly fact. It is with that in mind that we should turn our attention to some of the improbable (in the light of present knowledge) truths of science.

John Gribbin
May 2020

IMPROBABILITY

The Mystery of the Moon

A total eclipse of the Sun is one of the most spectacular and beautiful sights visible from the surface of the Earth. It is so spectacular because the Moon and Sun look the same size to us. So when the Moon passes in front of the Sun, it can exactly cover the bright solar disc, plunging the region affected by the eclipse into darkness, but allowing the glowing outer layer of the Sun, its corona, to become visible like a glorious halo. But why are we lucky enough to see this sight? Why are the apparent sizes of the Sun and Moon just right to produce it? The question is more profound than it seems at first, because the coincidence has not always held. Our human civilisation exists at a rare moment of astronomical time when the Moon is perfectly placed to make this kind of eclipse. In the not too distant geological past, it was too close to Earth and would have blotted out the corona as well; in the astronomical future it will be too far away and will look like a small dark blob passing across the solar disc. Improbably, it is 'just right' just at the time we are here to notice it.

A solar eclipse
Science Photo Library

But the effect only happens at all because the Moon is so large. As a fraction of the size of its parent planet (Earth), it is by far the largest moon in the Solar System. Indeed, many astronomers think that the Earth–Moon system should better be regarded as a double planet than as a planet plus a moon. And that is all down to the way the double planet formed.

The Sun and Solar System formed when a cloud of gas and dust in space collapsed under the pull of its own gravity. Most of the material went in to the central star, the Sun. Some of the dust, and icy particles, was left in a disc around the star, and particles of that dust collided and stuck together until some were big enough to tug other particles towards them by gravity, so that bigger and bigger objects built up. This eventually made the planets, but some material was left over to make smaller objects, asteroids and comets. The late stages of this process were far from gentle, as proto-planets were bombarded with debris as they swept their orbits around the Sun clear. Just a hint of what this bombardment was like can be gleaned from the battered face of the Moon; but this tells less than the full story, because the Moon itself only formed after most of the process of planet building had taken place.

It is straightforward to account for the moons that we see orbiting around other planets in the Solar System, such as Mars, Jupiter and Saturn. The moons of Mars are clearly small pieces of debris – asteroids – left over from the planet-building process and captured by Mars. The moons of giant planets like Jupiter and Saturn are much bigger than asteroids – but

3

the giant planets are much bigger than Mars. Their families of moons formed around the parent planets in the same way that the planets formed around the Sun, making miniature 'solar systems'. But the Moon is 25 per cent as big as the Earth, in terms of its diameter, and clearly formed in a different way. The best explanation is that within a few million years of the Earth forming, the planet was involved in a collision with another young planet, an object the size of Mars, which struck it a glancing blow. In the heat generated by this violent event, the incoming object would have been destroyed, and the proto-Earth's newly formed crust would have melted. The heavy metallic core of the incomer would have sunk to the centre of the Earth, mixing with Earth's own metallic heart to make a planet with a very dense core and a relatively thin crust. The crust would be thin because molten material from the impact, a mixture of stuff from the proto-Earth and the incomer – graphically referred to by astronomers as the Big Splash – would have been flung off into space, some escaping entirely but some staying to form a ring around the Earth from which the Moon coalesced. It is easy to remember how long this process took; computer simulations tell us that something resembling the Moon would have formed within a present-day month of the impact. Dating of lunar rock samples tells us that all this happened about 4.4 billion years ago. Among other things, the impact set the Earth spinning rapidly on its axis, and knocked it out of the vertical, causing the tilt which is responsible for the cycle of the seasons.

All of this explains many oddities about the Earth. The planet Venus, just sunward of the Earth, is roughly the same size as the Earth, but has a thick crust, a small metallic core, and as a result a negligible magnetic field. It rotates only once every 243 of our days. The Earth has a thin crust, a large metallic core that is responsible for a strong magnetic field, relatively rapid rotation, and a large Moon. These features go together like a hand in a glove. Our planet is the odd one out in the Solar System, produced by a highly improbable sequence of events, all linked to the Moon. And the consequences of those events are far-reaching.

Take the thinness of the crust. It might not sound like a big deal, but it is. The crust is so thin that it can crack like an eggshell, with the pieces of the shell being moved about by convection currents in the fluid layers beneath, in the process known as plate tectonics. Thanks to the thinness of the crust, around the edges of these pieces of shell (the plates) there is constant volcanic activity, releasing gases like carbon dioxide and water vapour into the atmosphere. Where the crust is cracked, usually under the oceans, new crust can be made as molten material wells up and sets, spreading out on either side of the crack, pushing the plates away on each side. But the Earth does not get any bigger, because in other parts of the world, especially along the edges of some continents, crust is being pushed down into the interior. This carries carbonates and water back down where they get fed into volcanoes and are released into the air again in an endless cycle.

But the cycle does not run at a constant speed. The process which takes gases like carbon dioxide out of the atmosphere is called weathering. Carbon dioxide dissolves in water, and then reacts with minerals in the rocks to make calcium carbonate (limestone). Carbon dioxide in the atmosphere is, of course, a greenhouse gas – it traps heat and keeps the surface of the Earth warmer than it would otherwise be. As it happens, weathering proceeds faster when the world is warmer, so that tends to draw carbon dioxide out of the air efficiently, allowing the planet to cool. But when it cools, weathering is less efficient, and carbon dioxide builds up in the air again. The world warms, and the weathering process speeds up, drawing more carbon dioxide out of the air. There is a negative feedback which, thanks to plate tectonics, helps to keep the temperature at the surface of the Earth in the range where liquid water can exist (although, unfortunately, these natural processes are too slow to compensate for the buildup of carbon dioxide now being caused by human activities quickly enough to save us from the consequence of our own folly). Without this process – without the thin crust produced by the impact that made the Moon – the Earth would probably have become a scorching desert with a thick carbon dioxide atmosphere, like our neighbour Venus.

This isn't the only thing we have to thank the Moon for. Analysis of seismic waves produced by earthquakes and travelling through the interior of our planet shows just how large the central core is. It is a solid lump of iron and nickel with a diameter of about 2,400 km, the top of which is about 5,200 km below the surface of the Earth. But it is surrounded by a layer of liquid material, extending a further 2,500 km upward, roughly halfway to the surface of the Earth from the top of the inner core. Together, the inner and outer core contain a third of the mass of our planet, part of it donated by the impacting object which produced the Moon. It is the outer core that is important to us, and to all life on Earth. The temperature in this iron–nickel liquid layer is about 5,000°C, only a little less than the temperature at the surface of the Sun, maintained by the radioactive decay of elements such as thorium and uranium, left over from the formation of the Solar System. Swirling currents in this layer generate the magnetic field of the Earth.

The Earth's magnetic field is literally a force field, which protects our planet from a major threat from space. The Sun produces a blast of electrically charged particles, blandly called the 'solar wind', which reaches out from its source across space and past the Earth and the other planets. These particles travel at speeds of several hundred kilometres per second most of the time, and up to 1,500 kilometres per second during outbursts known as solar storms. Without the shielding effect of the magnetic field which forms a protective layer around the Earth, these 'solar cosmic rays', essentially the same as the particle radiation from a nuclear bomb, could strip away the outer layers of the atmosphere and penetrate to the ground where they would cause considerable damage to life, possibly even sterilising the land surface of the planet.

7

The region around the Earth that is protected by the magnetic field is called the magnetosphere, but 'sphere' is actually the wrong term, because the solar wind is so powerful that it squashes the magnetic field on the side facing the Sun, while on the other side of the Earth the magnetic field is stretched out in a long tail, making an overall shape like a cosmic tadpole. On the side facing the Sun, the boundary between the magnetic field and the solar wind (the hull of Spaceship Earth) lies about 64,000 km above the surface of the Earth; on the side away from the Sun, it stretches out almost exactly as far as the distance to the Moon. And at the north and south magnetic poles, a small proportion of the particles of the solar wind leak in to the upper part of the atmosphere of the Earth. Most of the time, the only effect this has is to produce the beautiful displays known as the northern and southern lights. But during solar storms the effects at high latitudes can be damaging to anything that uses electricity. They disrupt communications, affect power lines, and cause blackouts in places such as Canada. If the magnetosphere suddenly failed, this would happen all over the Earth.

It is a sobering fact that there is geological evidence that just such events have occurred in the past, with the magnetic field fading away suddenly (by the standards of the geological timescale) then rebuilding, either in the same sense as before or with north and south magnetic poles reversed. The evidence comes from the magnetic record left in some kinds of rock as they solidify after volcanic eruptions. As the rock sets, the magnetic field gets frozen in to it, forming a permanent magnet preserving the direction of north and south at the time. The rocks can be dated by various techniques to show when the magnetic field gradually disappeared. And the fossil record of life on Earth shows that when the magnetic field is weak, many species of life on Earth go extinct, although creatures living in the oceans are not affected. The natural conclusion is that land dwellers were zapped by radiation from space, while sea dwellers were protected by layers of water. But even if this explanation is wrong, there is no escaping the evidence that land dwellers die out when the field is weak. The not-so-cheery news is that over recent decades the Earth's magnetic field has been weakening at a rate somewhere between about 5 per cent per century and 5 per cent per decade. If this continues, it could disappear some time between about 2,000 years and 200 years from now.

Partly because the Earth gained some of the heavy elements that make up the core during the Moon-forming impact, while lighter material splashed out into space, even though the diameter of the Moon is a quarter that of the Earth its mass is only one eightieth of the mass of the Earth. Even in those terms, however, this still makes it the largest moon in proportion to its planet in the Solar System.* Because of this,

....

* If you want to argue that Pluto is a planet and has a proportionately very large moon, Charon, my response would be that Pluto–Charon is a double planet.

9

the gravitational influence of the Moon on the Earth has been a major factor on our planet ever since the Big Splash. The most obvious manifestation of this influence today is in the tides, but these are just a feeble ripple in the sea compared with what they used to be.

Computer simulations tell us that when the Moon first formed it was orbiting only about 25,000 km above the Earth, compared with an average distance today of a bit more than 384,000 km. This would have raised enormous tides not just in any oceans that existed but in the 'solid' Earth as well, stretching and squeezing the rocks over a range of about a kilometre in a regular rhythm. At first, the heat generated by this process would have kept the rocks molten even after the Big Splash, so the tides actually involved oceans of lava. But the energy of that process came from the orbital energy of the Moon, and as the energy was lost, it made the Moon weaken its grip and move outwards while the tides got smaller. A solid crust had formed by about a million years after the collision that gave birth to the Moon.

Thanks to the impact, the Earth was also spinning rapidly then, so that a day was about five hours long when the Moon was young. Today, we have tides about a metre high roughly twice a day, every twelve hours or so, with variations caused by the local geography of coastlines. Just (a million years or so) after the Moon formed, there were tides several kilometres high about every two-and-a-half hours. Life emerged from the sea and moved on to the land about 500 million years ago, and even a hundred million years later, 400 million years ago, in a memorable numerical coincidence there were about 400 days in the year, because the Earth was still spinning about 10 per cent faster than it does today, each day then being only a little more than 21 hours long. But over the billions of years since the Moon formed, one thing has stayed reasonably constant – the tilt of the Earth. And once again we have the Moon to thank for that.

Spinning objects that have a tilt wobble, as anyone who has played with a child's top knows. But there is more than one kind of wobble. The Earth leans over in space by about 23.4 degrees from a line at right angles to the plane of the Earth's orbit around the Sun. As I have mentioned, this tilt was produced when the young Earth was struck by a Mars-sized object in the collision that created the Moon. Over the course of a year the tilt always points in the same direction, so as the Earth moves around the Sun sometimes it leans towards the Sun, and sometimes away from the Sun. This is not a wobble, as you can visualise if you pretend that it is the Sun moving around a stationary Earth. The tilt causes the cycle of the seasons – when one hemisphere is leaning towards the Sun it is summer there and winter in the opposite hemisphere, and when one hemisphere is leaning away from the Sun it is winter there and summer in the opposite hemisphere.

I was careful to say that the tilt always points in the same direction 'over the course of a year', because it does actually change slightly in a regular way over tens of thousands of years.

This really is a wobble, and has profound and improbable implications for life on Earth, which I discuss in Improbability Eight. But here I am more interested in why the wobble isn't bigger. This is, of course, thanks to the stabilising influence of the Moon's gravity. The planets (and moons) of the Solar System all tug on one another by gravity, producing an influence which changes as the planets move round their orbits, and smaller planets such as Earth and Mars are particularly susceptible to the combined influences of the largest objects in the Solar System, the Sun and Jupiter. If a planet like Earth or Mars was the only planet orbiting the Sun, it would go on its way without wobbling. But, improbable though it may seem, even small gravitational nudges from the Sun and Jupiter can induce big wobbles, through the process known as chaos, which features in Improbability Six.

Computer modelling tells us that on Mars, which has no large moon, the tilt can change suddenly by at least 45 degrees, and more slowly up to about 60 degrees, where 'suddenly' means over the course of about 100,000 years. We don't have to rely solely on the computer modelling, though, because the surface features of Mars have now been studied by orbiting spaceprobes in enough detail to confirm that over geological time this kind of change has indeed occurred. This gives us confidence in the predictions of the same kind of modelling applied to our own planet, which tell us that without the presence of the Moon the Earth could go from being nearly upright in its orbit to nearly flat, with a 'tilt' of almost 90 degrees, over as little as 100,000 years. The implications would be profound. With one pole pointing towards the Sun, that hemisphere would experience searing summer during which the Sun never set, while the opposite hemisphere froze over as the Sun failed to rise. Six months later the situation would be reversed. And the tropical regions would be in permanent twilight and never thaw at all. It is solely thanks to the presence of the Moon that nothing like this has happened since life emerged onto land (as we know from the fossil record), and probably for much longer than that (as we infer from the computer modelling).

It is, of course, too good to last. As the Moon slowly but steadily retreats from the Earth, its stabilising influence will get less and less. The Moon has been with the Earth and exercising that influence for a bit more than 4 billion years, and is now moving outwards at a rate of about 4 cm per year. The simulations tell us that in about 2 billion years from now its stabilising influence will be too weak to prevent Jupiter-induced toppling of the Earth. Which brings me back to the improbability I started with. The Sun is about 400 times bigger than the Moon, but it is also about 400 times further away from us than the Moon is. In the past, the Moon would have looked much bigger, and easily blotted out the Sun during an eclipse. But during the era of the dinosaurs there was nobody around to notice. In the not too distant future (long before that wobble occurs), a ring of sunlight will be visible around the edge of the Moon even during an eclipse. There may or may not be anyone around then to notice. How curious that intelligent beings who notice things like that should be around just at the moment of geological time that it is there to be noticed. Especially because we are only here at all because of the Moon and its influence on the Earth. Highly improbable – but not impossible, as the fact that I am telling you about it testifies.

IMPROBABILITY

The Universe Had a Beginning, and We Know When it Was

The idea of the Big Bang origin of the Universe is now so familiar that it has become a cliché. It has even been used in the UK to refer to the sudden deregulation of the financial markets under Margaret Thatcher. But the idea of a beginning to the Universe is so improbable that scientists never even considered it until about a hundred years ago, and it did not become firmly established until about 50 years ago.

To the ancients, looking out at the night sky, the Universe seemed eternal and unchanging. Right up until the 1920s, what we now know to be the Milky Way galaxy, an island of a few hundred billion stars, was thought to be the entire Universe, in which individual stars might be born, live and die but the overall appearance always remained the same, like a forest in which individual trees live and die without changing the overall appearance. The idea of an unchanging Universe was so ingrained that even Albert Einstein, usually willing to entertain new ideas, accepted it without question. When he applied the equations of his general theory of relativity to describe the behaviour of the entire Universe (all of space and time), he found that the mathematics said that the Universe could not be static, but must be either expanding or contracting. This seemed so improbable to him that he added an extra factor to the equations, called the cosmological constant, to hold everything still.

In the early 1920s, improved telescopes and photographic techniques led to the discovery that our Milky Way is not the entire Universe, but just one island of stars among many scattered through vast regions of space. But at first this still seemed to fit the idea of a static Universe, albeit on a bigger scale. Then, at the end of the 1920s, Georges Lemaître and Edwin Hubble independently discovered (from the famous redshift effect) that the galaxies (strictly speaking, clusters of galaxies) are moving apart from one another – that the Universe is expanding. This was interpreted as caused by a stretching of space, exactly in line with Einstein's equations *without* the cosmological constant. He later described introducing the constant as 'the biggest blunder' of his career. Improbable as it had seemed, the Universe really was expanding.

But did that mean it had a beginning? Not necessarily. Some cosmologists argued that because galaxies are moving apart today, then long ago they were packed together in one lump of stuff, a kind of cosmic egg, that exploded outwards. But another school of thought held that as the galaxies moved apart the empty space between them got filled in by new galaxies being created out of primordial energy. This continual creation of matter seemed no more extravagantly improbable than the idea that all the matter in the Universe had been created in one go in some kind of cosmic egg. The continual creation would allow for the Universe to be eternal and unchanging in its overall appearance even though it was expanding. This 'Steady State' model was championed by Fred Hoyle, who coined the term Big Bang in a BBC radio broadcast to highlight the distinction between the two ideas.* To Hoyle and other proponents of the Steady State idea, the idea of a definite beginning seemed too improbable to take seriously. They weren't the only ones, as it has turned out. Soon after the discovery that the Universe is expanding, in 1931 Albert Einstein turned his attention to the implications. He drafted a paper in which he came up with exactly the same idea that Hoyle developed a decade and a half later, and wrote:

> If one considers a physically bounded volume, particles of matter will be continually leaving it. For the density to remain constant, new particles of matter must be continually formed in the volume from space.

----

* It is often said that he meant this as a term of derision. He told me, however, that he was simply looking for a snappy expression as a contrast with the expression Steady State.

But he got distracted by other work and never finished the paper for publication. It languished in the archives until Cormac O'Raifeartaigh and Brendan McCann, of the Waterford Institute of Technology, came across it eight decades later and had it translated and published in English in 2014. So if anyone asks you who was the first person to come up with the Steady State/Continual Creation idea, the answer is Einstein!

The debate between the two camps raged through the 1950s and into the 1960s. What was needed was a test to distinguish between the predictions of the two ideas, and one was dreamed up, but not initially carried out, roughly at the same time the Steady State idea was first being developed. It essentially depended on the idea that if the Universe were smaller in the past, with everything squashed together more tightly, then it must also have been hotter then, in the same way that the air in a bicycle pump gets hotter when it is compressed. From basic physical principles, two young American researchers, Ralph Alpher and Robert Herman, calculated how hot the Universe must have been when it was as dense as the nucleus of an atom, at the time of the Big Bang,* and how hot the leftover radiation from the Big Bang must be today. In 1948, they published their conclusion that 'the temperature in the universe at the present time is found to be about 5 K',

....

* We call this density the Big Bang because we understand the physics of matter at such densities and everything since very thoroughly. How this hot, dense fireball arose (what happened before the Big Bang) is more speculative, but I shall look at the best explanation shortly.

18

which corresponds to minus 268 degrees Celsius. The idea was promoted by their senior colleague George Gamow, whose name is often linked with the calculation, although he did not carry it out.

The prediction was largely forgotten in the 1950s, but early in the 1960s – less than 60 years ago – Arno Penzias and Robert Wilson, working at a radio telescope owned by the Bell Laboratories, unexpectedly discovered that the Universe is filled with a sea of microwave radiation with a temperature of about 3 K, later determined more precisely to be close to 2.7 K. This was a double surprise because not only were they unaware of the work of Alpher and Herman, they were both supporters of the Steady State idea. But they had accidentally ruled this out as impossible. It was quickly realised that this must be the radiation predicted by Alpher and Herman, and that there really had been a Big Bang, improbable though that still seemed to many astronomers. So *when* had the Big Bang happened? How old is the Universe?

The original technique for working out the time since the Big Bang depended on measuring the speed with which galaxies seem to be moving away from us (easy) and measuring how far away they are (hard) so astronomers could work backwards to find out when everything was together in one place. This is trivial arithmetic – if a car travelling along a straight highway at 60 miles an hour is 30 miles away from its starting point, how long ago did it start? The 'speed' is measured directly from the redshift, which is a stretching of light caused by the

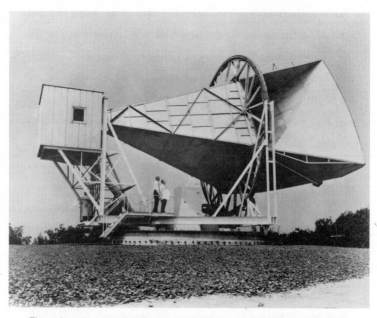

The radio telescope that Penzias and Wilson used to discover the CMB
NASA

expansion of the Universe. It is not a Doppler effect, despite what some accounts may tell you, because it is not measuring a speed through space, but the speed with which space itself is expanding, carrying galaxies along for the ride. The distances to galaxies are hard to measure, and this depends on knowing (or guessing) things like how bright galaxies are so the distance can be estimated from how dim they look to us – like measuring the distance to the end of the street by measuring how faint the light from a street lamp is. The relationship between speed and distance is described by a number called the Hubble constant, H. The bigger H is, the faster the Universe is expanding and the less time there has been since the Big Bang.

In the 1960s, when I started my career (such as it was) as an astronomer, the difficulty of working out distances to galaxies (the distance scale) meant that the best astronomers could do was to say that H must be somewhere between 50 and 100, and was probably about 75. For a value of 100, the age of the Universe would be a bit less than 9 billion years, while a value of 50 implies that it is twice as old, about 18 billion years. Quite separately, however, astrophysicists had been developing techniques to estimate the ages of stars, and were finding that the oldest known stars were significantly older than 9 billion years, which made the largest value of H suggested by cosmologists impossible.

Over the next few decades, improved measurements based on the traditional technique, culminating in studies made with the Hubble Space Telescope, pinned down the value of the

Hubble constant more and more accurately, culminating in a value of 72 ± 8 (that is, between 64 and 80), reported in 2001. But meanwhile, a completely different technique, using observations of the cosmic microwave background radiation, had also got a handle on the Hubble constant.

When the background radiation was first identified and astronomers took its temperature they found that it was exactly the same everywhere they looked – the temperature of the sky is the same in all directions. This matches the simplest predictions of cosmological calculations of the Big Bang, and among other things confirms that we do not live in a special place in the Universe, since this kind of pattern (or lack of pattern) would look the same from anywhere in the Universe. But as their measurements improved, and still no pattern was detected, this began to raise a nagging worry in the minds of cosmologists. Those simplest cosmological calculations actually described the behaviour of uniformly expanding spacetime without any matter in it. The real Universe contains galaxies of stars, and these must have grown out of irregularities that were present way back when the Universe was a hot fireball and the background radiation was much more intense. At that time, the fireball would have contained a sea of electrically charged particles, protons and electrons, interacting with the electromagnetic radiation of the fireball so that its temperature at any one spot depended on the density of the matter at that location. Then, as the Universe cooled to a temperature of a few thousand degrees (roughly the same as the temperature at the surface of the Sun today, but everywhere in the Universe) the protons and electrons got locked up in electrically neutral atoms, and the radiation 'decoupled'. It still carried the imprint of those primordial fluctuations but no longer interacted strongly with matter as it cooled all the way down to 2.7 K.

These primordial irregularities should have left an imprint on the temperature from different parts of the sky which could be detected today, if we had sensitive enough instruments to measure it. But they would have to be *very* sensitive. Working backwards from our measurements of the sizes of galaxies and clusters of galaxies today, astronomers were able to calculate how uneven the Universe was just after the Big Bang, at the time of decoupling. This meant they knew the size of the fluctuations in the temperature of the background radiation from place to place at that time, and could then work forwards again to calculate how big the differences in temperature from one part of the sky to another must be today. The answer turned out to be one part in 100,000. Which, for an average temperature of 2.7 K, meant that the instruments had to detect fluctuations of 0.00003 K, 30 millionths of a degree.

Improbably, measurements this accurate were made using a satellite called COBE (COsmic Background Explorer) launched by NASA in November 1989. Almost immediately, the instruments on COBE were able to measure the average temperature of the background radiation more accurately than ever before, and the result, 2.725 K, was presented at the January 1990 meeting of the American Astronomical Society.

But that was just the beginning. Over the course of more than a year, the instruments on board COBE scanned the entire sky, using three separate detectors. They took 70 million separate temperature measurements, which the team responsible for the mission then had to analyse, subtracting out the average temperature to produce a map which showed the tiny differences in temperature from one spot on the sky to another. The map was completed in 1992, and it revealed ripples in the background radiation, with hot spots on the sky 30 millionths of a degree warmer than average, and cold spots on the sky 30 millionths of a degree below average. But the average, remember, is just 2.725 K, so 'hot' and 'cold' are only relative terms. Traces of the irregularities which, under the influence of gravity, had grown to become galaxies had been found, providing more evidence in support of the Big Bang idea. But this alone did not provide an accurate independent measurement of the age of the Universe.

Inspired by the success of COBE, astronomers set out to squeeze even more information out of the background radiation. This involved searching for traces of so-called 'baryonic acoustic oscillations', which is jargon for sound waves – sound waves in the early universe that have left an imprint on the background radiation that might be detectable today.* These secondary ripples are smaller and harder to detect than the

---

* 'Baryon' is just the generic term for things like atoms, anything mostly made, in terms of mass, of protons and neutrons.

ones found by COBE, but they carry additional information which makes the effort of detecting them worthwhile. The exact pattern made by these ripples depends on a balance between the gravitational forces pulling huge clouds of gas together, and the influence of fast-moving particles of light (photons) of the background radiation during a short period of time, about 100,000 years, just after decoupling. This tended to smooth out irregularities. Some wavelengths of the sound get bigger during this interval while others are smoothed away. And this all happens in the expanding Universe, which both cools the photons (making them less energetic and reducing their influence) and stretches the acoustic waves, so that the speed with which the Universe is expanding, which depends on the Hubble constant, also comes in to consideration.

The result is a messy mixture of wavelengths, but astronomers are used to dealing with such mixtures and have a powerful tool, called power spectrum analysis, which can pick out the individual wavelengths that contribute to the messy overall picture. This is a bit like analysing the sound made by a symphony orchestra in full voice and working out what individual contributions are being made by the violins, the flutes, the percussion and all the other instruments. Another analogy would be analysing the sound that comes out of a church organ to work out the lengths of the organ pipes and other details of the structure of the instrument.

Power spectrum analysis of the pattern of tiny temperature fluctuations in the background radiation across the sky produces a wiggly graph, called (logically enough) the power spectrum, with a large peak on the left and a series of smaller and smaller wiggles tailing off to the right. The relative heights of the peaks in the graph provide a lot of data (not just about baryon acoustic oscillations, although they are particularly important) which reveals information about many features of the Universe, including the speed with which it is expanding and therefore the value of H and the age of the Universe. The key thing to remember is that this measurement is entirely independent of the traditional technique based on measuring the distances to galaxies.

The power spectrum of the microwave background was studied by two satellites in the early decades of the twenty-first century. First came NASA's Wilkinson Microwave Anisotropy Probe (known as WMAP and pronounced double-you-map), launched in the summer of 2001. The detectors on board WMAP were 45 times more sensitive than those on board COBE, and they could measure the temperature from individual patches of sky roughly one-fifth of a degree across, a third of the size of the full Moon as seen from Earth today. It operated until 2010, when it was moved to a parking orbit out of the way of any future satellites and switched off. Among the wealth of data it obtained (some of which comes into the story of Improbability Three) it initially measured the Hubble constant as 72 ± 5, corresponding to an age of the Universe (the time since the Big Bang) of 13.4 ± 0.3 billion years. As time passed and more data were gathered, including observations made by instruments carried on high-altitude balloons, this estimate of the age of the Universe was made even more precise and pushed up slightly to 13.772 ± 0.059 billion years. But by the time WMAP was being switched off and parked, another satellite, the European Space Agency's Planck probe, was picking up the baton.

Planck was launched in May 2009. With a sensitivity three times better than WMAP its instruments could measure differences in temperature from one spot on the sky to another as small as a millionth of a degree, while the size of the spots it measured was only one-twentieth of a degree across. Stop and think about that. It is easy to bandy about terms like a millionth of a degree. But in the second decade of the twenty-first century astronomers could look at a patch of sky one sixth of the apparent size of the full Moon, and tell you its temperature relative to its neighbours *to an accuracy of one millionth of a degree*. If that doesn't boggle your mind, nothing will.

Planck operated until 2013, when it followed WMAP into a parking orbit. It was in March that year, just before the satellite was retired, that the first detailed results from Planck were announced, indicating an age of the Universe of 13.819 billion years. A couple of years later, with more data analysed, the Planck team revised their estimate to 13.799 ± 0.021 billion years and a value of 67.74 ± 0.5 for the Hubble constant. This is not only very close to the number found by WMAP, but both satellites give values right in the range of 72 ± 8, reported in 2001 by the people using the traditional technique. In less than

60 years, astronomers had gone from arguing about whether the value of H is 50 or 100, corresponding to ages of 18 billion or 9 billion years, to quibbling about a difference in the second decimal place! That difference between the measurements made by WMAP and Planck amounts to no more than 100 million years out of roughly 14 *billion* years – less than 1 per cent.

This is one of the greatest – and most improbable – achievements of science. Any scientist, let alone a lay person, of any previous generation would have been dumbfounded to learn that we know the age of the Universe to within 1 per cent, and that it is 13.8 billion years, give or take a hundred million. But even this is not the end of the story. There is some icing to put on the cake.

I mentioned earlier that there was concern back in the 1960s (and even a little later) when some estimates of the age of the Universe came out lower than estimates of the ages of some stars. There is no longer any need for that concern. While cosmologists were busy refining their estimates of the age of the Universe, astrophysicists were equally busy refining their measurements of the ages of stars. With gratifying results.

There are now several different ways to measure the ages of stars, but I will briefly mention just two, to highlight how well astronomers now understand the Universe. The first depends on the discovery, made early in the twentieth century, of how the temperature of a star (which is linked to its colour) is related to its brightness. On a graph plotting brightness on the vertical axis and temperature going down from right to left along the horizontal axis, most stars lie on a line running from top left (hot and bright) to bottom right (cool and dim). The apparent brightness of a star depends on its distance, so these brightnesses are calculated from how a star would look at a distance of 32.5 light years (10 parsecs, in the units astronomers prefer). That in turn depends on knowing the distances to stars, which is why this relationship was not discovered sooner (just how astronomers measure distances to stars is a whole other story). The graph is called the Hertzsprung-Russell (or H-R) diagram, after the two astronomers who each independently discovered the relationship. Because most bright stars are on the top left to bottom right line, it is called the main sequence. But there are smaller numbers of stars below the line to the left (dim but hot) and above the line to the right (bright but cool).

The position of a star on the main sequence depends only on its mass. The more massive a star is, the faster it has to burn the nuclear fuel in its heart to hold itself up against its own weight, so it releases more energy and is very bright. But as its nuclear fuel is being exhausted, the outer regions of the star swell up, so all the heat is going across a bigger area, which makes the surface cool. The star becomes a red giant, in the upper right of the H-R diagram. When all its fuel is used up, it becomes a stellar cinder (a white dwarf), shrinking down and appearing in the bottom left of the diagram. But the key point is that the time in a star's life when this happens depends on its mass. So for a group of stars all the same age, the main sequence steadily gets shorter, as if the line was being rubbed out starting at the top left. In the memorable expression, 'big stars live fast and die young'. The relationship between mass and temperature of main sequence stars is very well understood, because whatever is holding the star up must produce exactly enough heat to stop it collapsing. Too much heat and the star would explode; too little and it would shrink. So the point where the main sequence ends tells us the mass of the oldest stars in that group, and that in turn tells us their age, because we know how long it takes for stars of different masses to use up their nuclear fuel (essentially by converting hydrogen into helium).

Putting all this together, if we have a group of stars all the same age, *and* we can measure the distance to them, *and* we can identify the top end of their main sequence, then we can work out the age of the group of stars. Fortunately, there are such groups, called globular clusters. These are spheres of stars which contain hundreds of thousands of individual stars. The stars in each cluster all formed together not long after the Big Bang, in the outer regions of the primordial cloud of gas from which our galaxy grew (similar clusters are seen around other galaxies). Unfortunately, working out the distances to them is very hard. But at least standard physics does tell us the ages of stars with different masses. With all the difficulties involved, even by the middle of the 1990s all the astrophysicists could say about the ages of globular clusters was that they must be between 12 and 18 billion years old. At least this was in the same ball park as cosmological estimates of the age of the Universe, but frustratingly vague. But then came the ESA satellite Hipparcos.

Hipparcos was launched in 1989, and made precision measurements of the distances to almost 120,000 stars, using the technique of parallax, the apparent shift in position of stars on the sky when they are measured from opposite sides of the Earth's orbit. The team described the accuracy of the measurements as equivalent to using a telescope on top of the Eiffel Tower to measure the size of a golf ball on top of the Empire State Building. Combining Hipparcos data with all other ways of measuring the ages of globular clusters, by the end of the 1990s Brian Chaboyer and other members of the Hipparcos team came up with a best estimate of the ages of the oldest globular clusters of 12.6 billion years, with an uncertainty of roughly plus or minus a billion. Data from a later satellite, Gaia, launched at the end of 2013, suggest a slightly higher figure, but still less than 13.8 billion years.

The second technique I want to mention is very, very simple in practice but horrendously difficult for the observers to carry out. It depends on the way radioactive elements 'decay' to produce a mixture of different elements. This process is very well understood from studies here on Earth, and is widely used for estimating the ages of rocks. Uranium-238 is one such useful radioactive element, and in any sample of U-238 half of the atoms decay in 4.5 billion years (roughly the same as the age of the Earth), half of the remainder decay in the next 4.5 billion years, and so on. The age of anything containing U-238 can be worked out by measuring how much U-238 it contains now and comparing this with the quantities of the various 'decay products' which tell us how much it started out with. 'All' the astronomers had to do was find a star with uranium-238 in its atmosphere and measure the amount of this and the various decay elements, using spectroscopy, the most powerful tool in astronomy.* This is what is horrendously difficult, but it has actually been done for a few stars, including a red giant called HS 1523-0901 which lies about 7,500 light years from Earth in the direction of the constellation Libra. It has an age of 13.2 billion years, plus or minus 3 billion years, reported by Anna Frebel in 2007.

In spite of the remaining uncertainties in the astrophysical estimates, everything matches the cosmological age determination. This is an even more profound fact than you may at first realise. The cosmological age of the Universe is determined from large-scale physics (mostly the general theory of relativity). The astrophysical age of the Universe is determined from relatively small-scale physics of how stars work, with no reference to the general theory at all. Yet they give the same answer. Clearly, science works! Physicists had entitled themselves to a pat on the back. But they cannot rest on their laurels, because at the beginning of the 2020s there appears to be a fly in the ointment. There is a small but possibly significant difference

....

* And described properly in my book *Seven Pillars of Science*.

32

between the determinations of the Hubble constant made using the traditional techniques and those made by studying the background radiation, which looks more worrying as the 'error bars' on the traditional measurement have been reduced. Proponents of each measurement technique insist that their numbers are accurate. But everything does not, after all, fit together quite perfectly. Cosmologists refer to this as 'tension' between the two camps, preferring not to use the word 'disagreement'. But this is the kind of fly physicists ought to welcome, since it points the way to new discoveries. And it just may be relevant to the next story I have to tell.

The Expansion of the Universe is Speeding Up

What was there before the Big Bang? How did the Universe begin? How will it end? Improbably, we have at least partial answers to all these questions. And they are all linked to one crucial property of the Universe – its density.

The equations of the general theory of relativity can be run backwards or forwards, to tell us both about the birth of the Universe and its fate. Looking back, they imply that there was a beginning to time and space, when everything that we can detect in the expanding Universe emerged from a point of zero volume and infinite density, a singularity at 'time zero'. Physicists do not believe that this really happened, because quantum effects do not allow such things to exist. But they do accept that something happened to produce a region of enormous density in a tiny volume that developed into the Big Bang. If we accept that the Big Bang was the time when the entire Universe was at the density of an atomic nucleus, which is the usual rule of thumb, it happened about one ten-thousandth of a second after the beginning of time; half an hour after time zero the temperature was still 300 million K, twenty times the temperature at the heart of the Sun. Everything that has happened to matter since the first one ten-thousandth of a second is explained by well-understood physics. But that first split second is crucial to an understanding of what happened later. And it is intimately related to a profound puzzle about the density of the Universe today.

Although the Universe is expanding, gravity is trying to slow the expansion and pull everything back together. Until about twenty years ago, this seemed to point to a few simple possibilities. Whether gravity will succeed in overcoming the expansion depends on how fast the Universe is expanding and how much matter it contains – its density. If the density is low enough, gravity will be too weak to stop the expansion, and it will carry on for ever. If the density is high enough, gravity will win, and the Universe will eventually stop expanding and begin to collapse back towards a singularity. And there is a unique special case, the so-called critical density, where the expansion gets slower and slower but never quite stops. But it turned out that this is not the whole story.

As Einstein explained, there is a relationship between mass and the way space and time are curved. In the language of the general theory, the ever-expanding version is said to be open, the recollapsing version is said to be closed, and the critical version is said to be flat. The curious thing about our Universe is that as far as we can tell it is, indeed, flat. Why is this curious? Because of what it implies about conditions at the time of the Big Bang, and because absolute flatness is the least likely of all the possibilities, requiring fine-tuning on a mind-boggling scale.

The density is defined by a number called the density parameter, with a value of 1 corresponding to the single critical density, smaller numbers to the infinite number of open possibilities and higher numbers to the infinite number of closed possibilities. Even before the advent of satellites that studied the background radiation, simply by counting the number of galaxies seen in the volume of space we can observe, astronomers knew that the density parameter today must have a value between 0.1 and 10. This sounds like a big range. But the parameter has changed as the Universe expanded away from the Big Bang, because of the changing balance between the density and the expansion rate, which each got smaller but at different rates. As a result, the way the Universe has expanded since the Big Bang continually pulled it away from the critical density. In order for that to lie between 0.1 and 10 today, it had to be precisely 1 to an accuracy of one part in 10^{60} at the time of the Big Bang. The satellite data made things even more puzzling, by revealing that the flatness parameter is indistinguishably close to 1 even today, so it must always have been indistinguishably close to 1 – or, not quite always. 'Only' since the first ten-thousandth of a second. And in that tiny fraction of a second lies the explanation for this improbable feature of the Universe.

As I have hinted, the effects of quantum physics become important for the entire Universe in the interval between time zero and the Big Bang. Among other things, this tells us that there is a quantum of time, the smallest amount of time it is possible to have. This is 10^{-43} seconds. The expansion of the Universe started not from a singularity at time zero ($t = 0$) but at that time, $t = 10^{-43}$ seconds, from a seed no bigger across than the so-called Planck length (10^{-35} m), when the density was not infinite but 'only' some 10^{94} grams per cubic centimetre.* These are the absolute limits on size and density allowed by quantum physics. You might think that such a tiny object with such a huge density would be crushed by gravity and disappear. But at the end of 1979 an American physicist, Alan Guth, realised that need not happen, and found a way to bridge the gap between the beginning of time and the Big Bang.

He noticed that a quantum process called symmetry breaking, which occurs under such extreme conditions, could release energy in the first split-second of time, providing a violent outward push which expanded the Universe so rapidly that gravity did not have time to make it collapse. The violent push soon turned off, but it produced the Big Bang and left the Universe to continue coasting outwards with gravity now able to start slowing the expansion. The release of energy involved

....

* The seed itself was probably a so-called quantum fluctuation, popping into existence out of nothing at all. See https://www.amazon.co.uk/Before-Big-Bang-Kindle-Single-ebook/dp/B00T6L43NY

in symmetry breaking is like the latent heat released by water when it changes from a vapour to a liquid, but much more extreme. At the beginning of time this process took each tiny region of space, far smaller than a proton, and 'inflated' it to the size of a basketball. And this made the Universe flat.

You can see how this happened from another analogy. The amount of inflation that happened just before the Big Bang was equivalent to taking a tennis ball and inflating it to the size of the entire visible Universe. A tennis ball is obviously curved, bent round into a sphere. But if it were as big as the Universe we see around us, any creatures moving around on its surface would think it was flat. In the same way, cosmic inflation has made the space of our Universe indistinguishable from flat space, with the density of the Universe indistinguishable from the critical density.

There's a bonus. In the late stages of inflation, quantum fluctuations in what Alan Guth has called 'the prequel to the Big Bang' produced tiny irregularities. These irregularities grew with the inflation, and were left as irregularities in the Big Bang, acting as the roots from which galaxies and clusters of galaxies could grow. This kind of fluctuation produces a characteristic pattern of bigger and smaller irregularities – and the satellites have shown exactly this kind of pattern imprinted on the background radiation. Even COBE detected this pattern, as well as showing that the Universe is flat, confirming the predictions of inflation theory. The Universe has precisely the critical density of matter. But that posed a puzzle in the 1990s. Where was all the matter needed to flatten the Universe?

By the 1990s, astronomers were well aware that as well as all the bright stars we can see in the Milky Way and other galaxies there must be other stuff that we can't see, dark material which does not shine by its own light but reveals its invisible presence by its gravitational influence on the way galaxies rotate and move around within clusters. But it had taken them a long time to accept the evidence for this.

The speed with which galaxies are moving relative to one another in clusters is worked out from another version of redshift, this time a genuine Doppler effect caused by motion through space. The first person to draw attention to this was the America-based Swiss astronomer Fritz Zwicky, in the 1930s. The random speeds of individual galaxies in a cluster may be more than 1,000 km per second, and they are only prevented from escaping from the cluster by the gravitational pull of all the matter inside the cluster. There has to be more than a certain amount of matter, otherwise the escape velocity from the cluster would be less than the speeds of the galaxies, and the cluster would evaporate as galaxies escaped. When Zwicky tried to balance the equations he found that bright galaxies provide just a small fraction of the mass of a typical cluster. Most astronomers found this so improbable that for decades they simply ignored Zwicky's findings.

Things started to change in the 1980s, after the American astronomer Vera Rubin and her colleagues studied the way individual galaxies rotate, by measuring the Doppler speeds of stars and other features at different distances out from the centre of each galaxy. They expected to see them rotate in the same way the Solar System does, with objects closer to the centre moving faster than ones toward the edge. This happens in the Solar System because most of the mass is concentrated in the centre, in the Sun, so planets further out feel a weaker pull. Because most of the stars, dust, and gas of a galaxy is concentrated in the middle, it seemed obvious that the stuff on the edges shouldn't feel much pull and should move more slowly than stuff near the centre. But Rubin found that disc-shaped galaxies like our Milky Way rotate at the same speed all the way out to the edge of the visible bright disc of stars. The only possible explanation was that the galaxies were each being held in the grip of huge halos of 'dark matter', containing about ten times as much mass as in the bright stars. Zwicky was vindicated. But (there always seems to be a but) this couldn't be the end of the story.

You might think that all this dark matter might be in the form of gas and dust, made up from atoms and molecules, just like ourselves, the Solar System and the bright stars like the Sun – so-called baryonic matter, all built up from protons, neutrons, and electrons. Some of the mass needed to stop galaxies escaping from clusters is indeed in the form of hot gas, which emits X-rays that are detected by satellites. But that isn't the whole story. The well-understood physics of the Big Bang, when conditions were 'only' as extreme as inside the nuclei of

Vera Rubin
Getty Images

atoms today, sets a strict limit on the number of baryons that could have been involved in interactions during the Big Bang. This tells us that the density of baryons in the Universe is no more than 5 per cent of the critical density needed to make the Universe flat. Applying this rule of thumb in the case of clusters of galaxies, there is a limit to how much baryonic matter there can be in a cluster. Even the combined mass of gas and galaxies and any other baryonic matter up to the limit allowed by this rule is still much less than the total cluster mass, showing that there is a great deal of other stuff, non-baryonic matter, around. Since this stuff is both cold and dark, it is known, logically enough, as cold dark matter. Nobody knows what this stuff is, but it is referred to as 'CDM' to make it sound more familiar. The important point is that it is not the same as the stuff we are made of, and it does not interact with baryonic matter except through gravity – it is dark because it does not interact with light or other electromagnetic radiation (such as radio waves or X-rays) at all. This is why it is not subject to the same Big Bang limits as baryonic matter, but that makes it very hard to detect directly, which is why we do not yet know what particles of CDM are like.

Here's the snag. By the mid-1990s it was clear that putting everything together, in order to hold clusters of galaxies together about 5 per cent of the critical density could be supplied by baryons, and about 25 per cent by cold dark matter. This only adds up to 30 per cent of the mass density needed to make the Universe flat. Where is the rest? The few cosmologists who worried about this in the 1990s called the problem the baryon catastrophe. But there was a solution. As I wrote in 1996,* summing up work by David White and Andy Fabian, of the Institute of Astronomy in Cambridge, 'if cosmologists wish to preserve the idea of a spatially flat Universe, as predicated by theories of cosmic inflation, they may have to reintroduce the idea of a cosmological constant'. The reason is that a cosmological constant, like the one Einstein introduced and then rejected when the Universe was found to be expanding, corresponds to an energy, or field, that fills space, and gives it a kind of springiness. This can act like a stretched spring, opposing the expansion of space and holding things back (the way Einstein originally thought of it) or like a squashed spring, pushing outwards against the influence of gravity and making the expansion faster, depending on the exact value of the constant. The Greek letter lambda (Λ) is used to denote the cosmological constant, which is sometimes referred to as a 'lambda field'. As mass and energy are equivalent, the lambda field affects the curvature of space. If the Universe is flat, and it contains only about 30 per cent of the matter needed to make it flat in the form of baryons and cold dark matter, then there is room for 70 per cent of the critical density to be in the form of a cosmological constant, or 'dark energy' as it became known. In 1996, this was an obscure and improbable suggestion known only to a few cosmologists (and

---

* *Companion to the Cosmos*, Weidenfeld & Nicolson, London, 1996.

at least one science writer). A couple of years later, the lambda field was all the rage.

It happened as a result of a serendipitous discovery. In the late 1990s two teams of researchers were trying to improve measurements of the Hubble constant by pushing the technology to measure the properties of exploding stars known as supernova type 1a, or simply SN1a. These are pretty rare; in a galaxy like the Milky Way there are only a couple every thousand years or so. But with thousands of galaxies to study, they are often detected, because for a brief time each one shines as brightly as the entire galaxy it lives in. This is a boon to cosmologists, because every SN1a peaks at the same brightness when it explodes. The brightness is calibrated by studying supernovas in nearby galaxies, whose distances have been found by other means. So when a supernova of this kind explodes in a galaxy far, far away its apparent brightness (or faintness) tells us exactly how far away that galaxy is. Measuring the redshift of the same galaxy then gives astronomers a value for the Hubble constant.

The aim of the two teams was to use this technique, averaged over very many galaxies, to study faint and distant galaxies. Because light takes a finite time to travel through space, when we look at distant galaxies we are seeing light which left them long ago – billions of years ago – when the Universe was younger and more compact. Because gravity tries to hold back the expansion of the Universe, the researchers expected that by comparing their studies of very distant galaxies harbouring SN1a with similar studies of nearby galaxies they would find out how much faster it was expanding in the past, before gravity had had much time to slow it down. To their utter astonishment, in 1998 both teams found that their measurements implied that the Universe was expanding more *slowly* in the distant past – or, putting it the other way round, that it is now expanding faster than it used to. The expansion of the Universe is accelerating.

It is just as well that two teams independently came up with the same conclusion, using entirely independent observations, because to most astronomers this seemed so improbable that if only one team had announced the discovery it would probably have been regarded as a mistake. As it was, the mysterious acceleration was attributed to the phenomenon of dark energy (like CDM, simply a term to disguise the fact that nobody knew what it was), and theorists briefly had a field day trying to come up with exotic explanations for it.* But there was no need. The simplest and most likely explanation for dark energy was already under their noses. I mean the lambda field, of course; the modern manifestation of Einstein's cosmological constant. As we have seen, this contributes a springiness to the Universe, pushing outwards while gravity pulls inwards. In effect, the baryon catastrophe predicted the accelerating expansion, because the amount of dark energy needed to explain the SN1a results is exactly the same as the

....

* Some of them still do. Well, it keeps them occupied.

amount needed to make the Universe flat. And the way the lambda field works also explains why the Universal expansion has only recently (in cosmological terms) started to speed up.

Apart from its actual value, the key property of the lambda field is that it is not only the same everywhere, but the same at all times. Because it is a property of space, each cubic centimetre of space – not just 'empty space' out there among the stars, but the 'space' occupied by the Sun, the Earth and other material things including yourself – contains the same amount of dark energy even if the Universe gets bigger and there are more cubic centimetres of space. So the outward push provided by the field stays the same as the Universe expands. But the inward tug of gravity weakens as the Universe expands and galaxies get further apart. Just after the Big Bang, the influence of gravity was strong enough to overcome the lambda field and slow the expansion. But there came a time when there was a kind of crossover, as the influence of gravity became weaker than the lambda field. At that time, the expansion started to accelerate. This happened about 4 billion years ago, round about the time the Sun and Solar System formed (but that is entirely coincidental).

It is straightforward to work out how much everyday matter you would need, spread out evenly across the Universe, to make it flat. It is roughly 10^{-29} grams per cubic centimetre, equivalent to just five atoms of hydrogen in every cubic metre of space. Of course, everyday matter is not distributed in this way, it is clumped together in galaxies and clusters of galaxies. But everyday matter only contributes 5 per cent of the required density anyway. More than two-thirds of the critical density comes from the lambda field (aka dark energy), which really does contribute the equivalent of nearly 10^{-29} grams per cubic centimetre evenly across the Universe. There is no way to measure this in laboratories here on Earth, and even a sphere as big across as the Solar System out to Neptune contains only the same amount of dark energy as the amount of energy released by the Sun in three hours.

If this is all there is to the Universe, and nothing changes, then the acceleration will get faster and faster, eventually tearing all material objects apart in what has been called the 'Big Rip'. It is just possible (excitingly so) that the 'tension' referred to in Improbability Two is telling us that what is now the standard model of the Universe, referred to as ΛCDM,* is missing something, and that there is a different fate in store. But I have no intention of speculating further in that direction, and will leave you with a summary of what is now the ΛCDM 'best buy' model of the Universe. The present value of the Hubble constant is 67.4 ± 0.5, the total density of baryons plus CDM is 31 per cent of the critical density, and the lambda field contributes the rest, 69 per cent. About one sixth of the matter density is provided by baryons; the stuff we are

---

* Notice that this shorthand term for the standard model doesn't even mention baryons; the stuff we are made of is such an insignificant fraction of the Universe it got left out.

made of and everything we can see, feel and touch, as well as everything directly observed with our telescopes, makes up, in round numbers, 5 per cent (one twentieth) of the Universe. If that doesn't sound improbable today, it certainly did 25 years ago when the baryon catastrophe first caught the attention of cosmologists.

IMPROBABILITY

We Can Detect Ripples in Space Made by Colliding Black Holes

Measuring the age of the Universe as 13.8 billion years with an error of no more than a hundred million years – less than 1 per cent – is, to say the least, impressive. But at the other end of the size scale, physicists can measure displacements in detectors 4 km long that amount to roughly one ten-thousandth of the width of a proton. This seemingly impossible (but actually only highly improbable) achievement was necessary for them to be able to detect ripples in space predicted by Einstein's general theory of relativity – gravitational waves.

A useful way to think about the relationship between matter, space, and gravitational waves involves imagining a heavy weight placed on a stretched rubber sheet like a trampoline and jiggled about. My version of the story has appeared with minor variations in several of my books,* so look away now

....

* Most recently here: https://www.amazon.co.uk/Discovering-Gravitational-Waves-Kindle-Single-ebook/dp/B071FFJT74

if you don't want to see it again. The key thing to think about here is how fast a gravitational influence reaches out across the Universe.

The presence of any object that has mass distorts space around it, and we can represent a mass like the Sun as a bowling ball plonked on the hypothetical trampoline. The ball makes a dent on the surface, and marbles rolled across the surface follow curved lines around the dent. Similarly, the curved space around a massive object such as the Sun makes things (even light) follow curved paths, as if there was a force (gravity) tugging them towards the Sun. It was Einstein's prediction of how much starlight would be bent as it passed near the Sun that enabled astronomers to confirm the accuracy of his general theory during a solar eclipse in 1919, making Einstein famous.

But what if the bowling ball is taken away? The curved surface of the trampoline becomes flat again, but it doesn't do so instantly. The smoothing out spreads across the surface. The Earth is following an orbit around the Sun because of the dent the Sun makes in spacetime.* If the Sun suddenly ceased to exist, the Earth would not immediately fly off into space, because the dent would still be there for a while, until there had been time for the news that the Sun had gone to reach us.

....

* I have to be careful here not to say that it is just a dent in space; the situation is a bit more complicated than the bowling ball analogy, but I shall not go into the details.

Einstein already knew, from the special theory of relativity, that nothing could travel faster than light; so he expected that gravity would travel at the same speed. If the Sun disappeared, the Earth would continue in its orbit, and the sky would be bright for another eight and a bit minutes, then the sky would go dark and the planet would fly free at the same time.

But remember the bowling ball being taken off a trampoline. The stretched surface doesn't instantly go back to being flat; it bounces up and down for a bit as it settles down, sending ripples across the surface. If the Sun disappeared, the space (spacetime) around it would presumably ripple in the same way, with the ripples dying down while it smoothed out. The ripples would be gravitational waves. After a false start when he made a mathematical slip, Einstein published the idea in 1918. But he was never quite sure if the effect was real, and once said: 'If you ask me whether there are gravitational waves or not, I must answer that I do not know. But it is a highly interesting problem.' Exactly a hundred years after he published the idea, however, such ripples were detected on Earth for the first time.

The detection required a huge effort, but one reason why physicists were sure the effort was worthwhile was because by then they had direct evidence of the effects of gravitational radiation on the behaviour of pairs of stars known as binary pulsars. Pulsars are rapidly spinning neutron stars – balls of matter only about 10 km across but with the density of an atomic nucleus, containing about as much mass as our Sun, left over when some stars much bigger than the Sun explode as supernovas. We can detect them because they have strong magnetic fields and beam out radio waves, like the beam from a lighthouse. Some of these beams flick across the Earth and can be detected, but there must be many pulsars whose beams are not oriented in the right direction for us to see them.

In 1974 Russell Hulse, a PhD student at Harvard University, was using a giant radio telescope at Arecibo in Puerto Rico (it featured in the movie *Contact*) to carry out a search for pulsars, under the supervision of Joseph Taylor. On 2 July 1974 he found a pulsar right at the limit of the telescope's capacity to make identifications, and after checking carefully over the next few weeks, he confirmed that it was a genuine discovery, and labelled the object PSR 1913+16. It proved to be an extreme example of its kind. The neutron star was spinning once every 58.98 milliseconds, making it the second-fastest pulsar known at the time, so that the beam produced seventeen blips in Hulse's detector every second.

But as Hulse continued to observe the pulsar, he found that it was changing in what seemed to be an impossible way. The measurements revealed a complicated pattern of behaviour. Sometimes the pulses arrived a little sooner than expected; sometimes a little later than expected. These variations changed smoothly and over a repeating period of 7.75 hours. Hulse realised that the changes could only be caused by the pulsar orbiting around another star. The speed with which the changes were taking place showed that the orbit of PSR

1913+16 must be tiny, which meant that its companion must be tiny – another neutron star. The two stars must actually form a binary pair, with similar masses, each star orbiting around their common centre of mass. So it became known as 'the binary pulsar', although only one of the neutron stars is detected as a pulsar.

This is an extreme system, making it an ideal testbed for the predictions of the general theory. Continuing observations showed that as the pulsar orbits its companion once every 7 hours 45 minutes, with an average speed of 200 kilometres per second, it reaches a maximum speed of 300 kilometres per second – a thousandth of the speed of light. The distance round the orbit is roughly 6 million kilometres, which is, coincidentally, about the same as the circumference of the Sun. So if the orbit of the binary pulsar were circular the whole system would fit inside the Sun, with the two neutron stars about the same distance apart as the distance from the centre of the Sun to its surface. As it happens, though, the orbits are elliptical, so the *pas de deux* danced by the two stars is more complicated. At their closest the two objects are about 1.1 solar radii apart; at maximum separation they are 4.8 solar radii apart. This is almost a textbook setup for producing gravitational waves.

You can see why if you imagine two hollow metal spheres, connected by a short rod, floating in a tank of water. If they do not move, there will be no waves in the water. But if they are rotating around one another, like a spinning dumbbell, waves will ripple out across the surface. The same sort of thing happens to spacetime when two neutron stars separated by less than the diameter of the Sun are orbiting around one another. But making waves requires energy. As energy from the binary pulsar is going into the gravitational waves, the two stars have to spiral together to give up gravitational energy, moving faster as they do so. The orbital period will decrease ('decay') by a tiny amount which can be precisely calculated from the general theory.

The prediction was that the orbital period of the binary pulsar, which is about 27,000 seconds, would decrease by about 0.0000003 per cent, or 75 millionths of a second, each year. In order to measure such a tiny effect, the astronomers had to make allowances for all kinds of influences, including the motion of the Earth in its orbit around the Sun and changes in the rotation of the Earth itself. Taking all these effects into account, after analysing roughly 5 million pulses from PSR 1913+16, in December 1978 Taylor was able to announce that the orbit of the binary pulsar was decaying exactly in line with the predictions of the general theory. The general theory is right, and gravitational waves are real. More than 50 binary pulsars are now known, providing even more evidence in support of the accuracy of the general theory, but the one discovered by Hulse and Taylor is still referred to as 'the' binary pulsar.

By the end of the 1970s, there was no doubt that gravitational waves do exist. But that left the enormous challenge of detecting gravitational waves directly, here on Earth. To most people, it looked impossible, because by the time waves from something like a binary pulsar reach us the ripples are much, much smaller than the size of an atom. But there are cosmic events which, theory predicts, should produce significantly bigger waves, and that offered a chink of hope for the experimenters.

That hope rested upon the possibility of detecting gravitational waves using the technique of interferometry. This literally depends on the way two things (such as light beams, in the laboratory version of such experiments) interfere with one another. Here comes another of my familiar analogies. When a pebble is tossed into a calm pond, ripples spread out smoothly in all directions. But if you toss two pebbles into the pond at the same time, you get two sets of ripples which interfere with one another, making a more complicated pattern. In some places the waves cancel out to leave the surface more or less flat; in other places the waves add together to make extra high ripples. This process may be familiar to you from a classroom experiment with light, designed to demonstrate how it behaves like a wave. In a darkened room a beam of light is shone through two small holes in a screen (a piece of paper or card is good enough for the job) and shone on to a second screen. The light waves spreading out from each hole in the first screen interfere just like those ripples on a pond, producing a pattern of light and shade on the second screen – an interference pattern. Physicists realised that in principle this kind of interference could be used to measure very small changes that would be produced by a gravitational wave squeezing and stretching the space between two objects. But putting the principle into practice would be difficult and expensive. The long saga involving a mixture of politics, science and personality clashes that followed this realisation has been entertainingly described by Janna Levin, in her book *Black Hole Blues*;* but I shall cut to the chase and describe the outcome of all these shenanigans.

Interferometry can be applied to the search for gravitational waves because of the way these waves distort spacetime. They do not produce ripples in the direction the wave is moving, the way water waves do, but change the shape of space at right angles to the direction the wave is moving. This squeezes space in and out in a regular way. When one direction is being squeezed the direction at right angles to the squeeze is stretched, and vice versa. So physicists realised that if they had a detector with two arms at right angles to each other, like a capital letter L but with both arms the same length, a gravitational wave passing through it would squeeze one arm at the same time it was stretching the other. These changing lengths provide a characteristic 'signature' of gravitational waves, which could be monitored using interferometry, if the arms were long enough and the detectors sensitive enough.

....

* Bodley Head, London, 2016.

The light required for the job has to come from lasers, which produce very pure beams with very precise wavelengths. The laser light has to be split into two beams, which are precisely in step with one another; these are then sent along the two arms of the experiment at right angles to each other but precisely the same length, before being reflected back along the same paths to merge again and make an interference pattern, monitored by an automatic system. If the experiment is perfectly set up, the returning waves will cancel each other out, and the monitoring system will detect nothing at all. But when a gravitational wave passes through the experiment, one arm is squeezed and the other stretched, so that the two beams get out of step. The resulting interference can be recorded, and even displayed on a monitor screen as wiggly lines, equivalent to the pattern of light and shade produced in the classroom experiment with two holes.

An obvious question is, how do the laser beams detect the stretching and squeezing of space, when they also are affected by the gravitational waves, being stretched and squeezed just like everything else? The answer lies in the fact that we are really dealing with spacetime, not just space. The distortion of spacetime affects how long it takes for the light beams to get from one end of the experiment to the other. What the interferometer actually measures is a time difference, not a space difference; but it is a simple matter to convert that into the spatial equivalent.

A formal proposal for a gravitational wave detector was

put forward in the USA in 1983. Nothing short of ambitious, it proposed a pair of identical detectors at widely separated locations. The idea was that gravitational waves would affect both detectors in the same way, with a small time delay, which meant they could be distinguished from local disturbances which affected each individual detector. The original proposal envisaged that each detector would have arms 10 km long, and the project would cost $70 million. The American National Science Foundation gave it the go-ahead in 1986, but the size of the arms of the two detectors had to be limited to 4 km, because the available sites were not big enough for anything more. Construction began in the mid-1990s, but to nobody's surprise, although the detectors were smaller the costs got bigger, soaring above $1 billion. Arguably, the most improbable feature of the whole project is that it ever got funded! The detectors were built at sites just about as far apart as possible within the contiguous United States, at Hanford, in Washington State, and Livingston, in Louisiana. What became known as the Laser Interferometer Gravitational-wave Observatory (LIGO) was the most expensive project ever funded by the NSF, which meant that there were many sighs of relief when, improbably, it actually discovered something, in September 2015. But the way in which the discovery was made is as intriguing as the fact of the discovery itself.

While the detectors were being built and tested, the theorists worked out exactly what kind of 'signal' they might detect, using computer simulations based on the general

The LIGO detection site at Livingston, Louisiana
Caltech/MIT/LIGO

theory of relativity.* Their best bet was the collision and merger of two black holes. This occurs inevitably in any binary system similar to the binary pulsar (indeed, it will inevitably happen, eventually, to the binary pulsar itself) as its component parts spiral together, but black holes are more massive than pulsars and will produce a bigger burst of waves. But while they were at it, the theorists also calculated what might be observed when two neutron stars merge. Simulations of how a pair of black holes would spiral together and merge were carried out for a variety of different black hole masses. They discovered that, if Einstein's equations are right, such a merger will produce a distinctive feature which they called a 'chirp', of gravitational waves, in which the ripples get shorter and shorter in wavelength (higher in pitch, in musical terms) as the black holes get closer and closer together, then ending abruptly as they merge into one object. In audible terms, this would be like the sound you make by running your hand rapidly along the keys of a piano from left to right. So the experimenters knew exactly what they were looking for. But as if their work wasn't hard enough already, they had set themselves a deadline. Einstein had finished his general theory in November 1915 and it was formally published early in 1916, which was also the year he first found a hint that the theory

....

* Astronomers use the term 'signal' to refer to any burst of light or other radiation from space, such as the radio noise from pulsars; there is no implication that an intelligence is producing it.

predicts the existence of gravitational waves. The LIGO team decided that it would be rather nice if they could detect such waves in 2016, a hundred years after the publication of the general theory. Improbably, and to their own surprise, they did better than that.

The details of the detector systems are mind-boggling. Light from a 20-Watt laser goes down each of the 4-kilometre-long arms through an evacuated tube a metre in diameter. At the ends of the tubes special partially reflecting mirrors bounce the light to and fro about 280 times before it is released into the interferometer set-up, effectively boosting the power of the detector. But since the prediction of the theorists was that the waves they were looking for would change the mirror spacing by only about 10^{-18} m, less than one thousandth of the diameter of a proton, the mirrors had to be shielded from any form of outside vibration, ranging from traffic on nearby roads (including staff bicycling in to work) to the movement of weather systems on the other side of the continent, the movement of currents in the Pacific Ocean, and just about every significant earthquake on Earth.

This was achieved by suspending each of LIGO's 40 kg test masses (heavy weights to which the mirrors are attached) in a system of four pendulums. Part of this suspension was 'passive', simply allowing the building to move around it while the test masses hung below. But the really clever bit was an 'active' system, which measured seismic disturbances and very gently pushed the other way to cancel them out, the way noise-cancelling headphones respond to sounds from outside and cancel them out.

With everything in place and tested, the first proper science run of the detectors was planned for September 2015. In order to be ready, a test run to make sure all these systems were working was being carried out in the middle of the night on Monday, 14 September. During a pause in those tests, the detectors were left in observing mode, although nobody was expecting to observe anything. But at 2.50am local time in Hanford, and 4.50am local time in Livingston, almost simultaneously, each detector recorded a chirp lasting 200 milliseconds. The detectors had picked up a gravitational wave signal far stronger than anyone had expected, and far more quickly than they had anticipated. Because there was a delay of just 6.9 milliseconds between its arrival at the first detector and its arrival at the second detector, this confirmed that the wave travelled at the speed of light.

The details of the chirp match the predictions for the spiralling together and merger of two black holes, one with about 29 times the mass of our Sun and the other about 36 times the mass of the Sun, to make a single black hole with a mass of about 62 times the mass of the Sun. The 'lost' mass tells us that about three times the mass of our Sun was converted into energy in the form of gravitational waves in the process. This is equivalent to 10^{23} times (a hundred billion trillion times) the luminosity of the Sun.

After checking and double-checking their observations to make sure there was no mistake, the team officially announced their discovery on 11 February 2016, almost exactly a hundred years after the general theory of relativity was announced to the world. But even before the news broke, LIGO detected a second black hole merger, which shook the detectors on Christmas Day 2015.* It was caused by the merger of black holes with fourteen and eight times the mass of the Sun, combining to make a black hole with a mass 21 times that of the Sun, with about one solar mass of matter being converted into energy. This showed that the first detection was not a fluke.

Since 2015, gravitational wave astronomy has become almost routine. The detection of another black hole merger is no longer news, just as the discovery of another planet orbiting a distant star is no longer news. But one other kind of merger is worth mentioning.

There is now a third gravitational wave observatory operating, a European detector called Virgo (after the constellation), similar to LIGO. With three working observatories on the ground, scientists can more precisely identify the region on the sky where gravitational waves come from. Similar detectors will soon come online in Japan and India, but three was enough to make a spectacular discovery in the summer of 2017. In August that year, all three gravitational-wave detectors saw a signal identified as a binary neutron star merger

....

* Christmas Day in the United States. Astronomers generally quote times in a system which is essentially the same as GMT; that puts it in the early hours of 26 December 2015, so it is often referred to as the Boxing Day event.

that occurred between 85 million and 160 million light years away. The combined mass of the two colliding stars was about three times the mass of our Sun. Because they could triangulate the source, the gravitational wave astronomers were able to tell other astronomers where to point their telescopes to see if they could spot anything interesting associated with the event. Within hours, five groups had identified a new source of light in a galaxy known as NGC 4993. This faded from bright blue to dim red over the next few days, and a couple of weeks later it began to emit X-rays and radio waves. Spectroscopic studies of the fading light showed that the violent outburst associated with the neutron star merger (called a hypernova) had produced huge quantities of heavy elements, including, to the delight of headline writers, gold. This solved a long-standing mystery.

As I described in my book *Seven Pillars of Science*, before 2017 astronomers knew that gold and other heavy elements could be produced in another kind of stellar explosion, supernovas; but they also knew that it was impossible for these events to make all the heavy elements we see in the Universe. Hypernovas turn out to be able to make just enough heavy elements to fill the gap. The event seen in August 2017 alone produced between three and thirteen Earth masses of gold, and similar events account for at least half the gold that there is in the Universe today. Improbable though it may seem, this means that much of the gold in any jewellery you possess was manufactured when neutron stars collided and merged.

IMPROBABILITY

*

Newton, the Bishop, the Bucket, and the Universe

This seems like a good place to stand back from cutting-edge twenty-first-century science and catch our metaphorical breath by looking at a more philosophical (or metaphysical) improbability, which taxed the brain of no less a thinker than Isaac Newton. As well as Newton, it involves a bucket of water, a long rope, and a bishop – which sounds like the beginning of a joke, but actually leads to a Deep Truth about the nature of the Universe, which helped Albert Einstein to develop the general theory of relativity.

You don't actually need a bucket to get a handle on what the puzzle is all about. It is visible in all its glory every time you stir cream into your coffee and watch the pretty patterns it makes as it swirls around. How does the cream, and the

....

* This section revisits some ideas discussed in the first edition of my book *In Search of the Big Bang*, but left out of later editions as they were regarded as too much of a diversion from the main story there. Suitably revised, though, they seem to fit perfectly here!

coffee, 'know' it is swirling around? You might guess that it is because it is moving past the side of the cup. But there is far more to it than that.

Newton was the first person to realise the implications (and for all I know he did get the idea from watching coffee swirling in a cup, since coffee drinking was very fashionable in his day). But Galileo seems to have been the first person to point out a closely related feature of the world – that it is not the speed with which an object moves but its acceleration that reveals the presence of forces acting upon it. On Earth, because of friction, wind resistance, and other influences that can never be got rid of, there are always outside forces trying to slow down a moving object. We have to keep pushing to keep it moving. But in space, as we have all seen in TV broadcasts by astronauts, things keep moving in a straight line until they feel the effect of a force. The nearest we can come to this on Earth is the motion of an ice hockey puck skimming across the ice, or (slightly less like motion in space) the puck on an air hockey arcade game. This really does seem to keep moving in a straight line at constant speed (that is, at constant velocity) until an outside force interferes with it. It was Newton who, without the benefit of ever seeing those TV broadcasts, worked out the law that the acceleration produced by a force is equal to the force divided by the mass of the object, and extended this (with the aid of his law of gravity) to explain the orbits of the planets around the Sun. In modern terminology, a frame of reference in which things move with constant velocity unless acted upon by external forces is called an inertial frame, and Newton had the idea that there must be some fundamental inertial frame, an absolute standard of rest, which is somehow determined by empty space. He argued that things move at constant velocity *relative to empty space* unless they are accelerated by outside forces.

There's an obvious snag with this idea. How do you know what empty space is? You can't hammer a nail into it and then measure all your velocities relative to the nail. How can you identify this absolute standard of rest? This is where the bucket comes in. Newton thought that he could use it to identify the fundamental inertial frame, as he described in his great book the *Principia*:*

The effects which distinguish absolute motion from relative motion are, the forces of receding from the axis of circular motion ... if a vessel, hung by a long cord, is so often turned about that the cord is strongly twisted, then filled with water, and held at rest together with the water [then let go]; thereupon, by the sudden action of another force, it is whirled about the contrary way, and while the cord is untwisting itself ... the surface of the water will at first be plain, as before the vessel began to move; but after that,

* The translation of Newton and the quotation from Berkeley below are taken from *The Unity of the Universe*, Dennis Sciama, Faber & Faber, London, 1959.

the vessel, by gradually communicating its motion to the water, will make it begin sensibly to revolve, and recede by little and little from the middle, and ascend to the sides of the vessel, forming itself into a concave figure (as I have experienced*), and the swifter the motion becomes, the higher the water will rise.

If the 'vessel' is then grabbed suddenly and held still, the water inside will still be rotating, and still rise up the sides, only gradually slowing down and flattening out, like the coffee stirred in your cup. It is not the relative motion of the bucket and the liquid that matters, but the absolute motion of the liquid relative (Newton thought) to empty space. When the bucket is rotating but the water is still, the surface is flat. When the water is rotating and the bucket is still, the water surface is curved. And when both are rotating, with no motion relative to one another, the surface is curved. In a modern version of the experiment, you could stand your cup of coffee dead centre on a turntable and watch it rotate. Both cup and liquid would be rotating, but the liquid would still form a concave surface. The liquid 'knows' it is rotating and acts accordingly. Philosophers who objected to Newton's argument and to the idea of absolute space on the grounds that something completely unobservable cannot be real had to find another way to explain what

* An important point. Newton actually did the experiment, it wasn't just an imaginary 'thought experiment'.

was going on in Newton's bucket. It took them 30 years, but then George Berkeley, an Irishman who was born in 1685 (the year before the publication of the *Principia*) and grew up to become a philosopher, economist, mathematician, physicist, and bishop (not necessarily in that order, to paraphrase Eric Morecambe) came up with an answer.*

Berkeley said that all motion must be measured relative to something. Newton's 'absolute space' is literally nothing, and cannot be perceived, so it doesn't fit the bill. As he put it, 'there is no space where there is no matter'. He pointed out that if everything in the Universe were annihilated except for a single globe (let's call it the Earth), then it would be impossible to envisage any motion of that globe, either through space, or as a rotation. There would be nothing to measure against, so movement would be meaningless. Even if there were two perfectly smooth globes in orbit around one another, there would be no way to measure that motion. But 'suppose that the heaven of fixed stars were suddenly created and we shall be in a position to imagine the motions of the globes by their relative position to the different parts of the Universe'. So 'it suffices to replace absolute space by a relative space determined by the heaven of fixed stars'. According to Bishop Berkeley, the coffee stirred in your cup rises up the sides because it knows that it is rotating *relative to the distant stars*. There's another example which many people have seen today. Science museums often

---

* Berkeley, California, was named in his honour.

contain a great Foucault pendulum, swinging ponderously to and fro. Such a pendulum keeps swinging in the same plane, while the Earth rotates underneath it, so that to us it seems as if the plane of the pendulum is rotating while we are standing still. The pendulum 'knows' where it is relative to, in Berkeley's terminology, the fixed stars, and holds itself steady compared with them and (we now know) the Universe beyond the stars.

But how does it know? What mysterious influence can reach out across space to affect the motion of water in a bucket, or a swinging pendulum, here on Earth? With no answers to these questions, Berkeley's idea did not gain wide currency during his own lifetime or in the century and a half that followed. But it was revived in the second half of the nineteenth century by Ernst Mach, the physicist whose name is immortalised in the number used to measure speed relative to the speed of sound.

Mach was born in 1838 in what was then the Austro-Hungarian Empire. He earned his PhD at the University of Vienna, and became a professor at the University of Prague in 1867 before returning to Vienna in 1895. He died in 1916, the year that Einstein published his general theory of relativity; but there is more than this calendrical coincidence to link him with that theory. It was while he was working in Prague that in 1883 Mach published a book, *Die Mechanik*, which took the puzzle of absolute motion a stage further, denying the reality of either 'absolute space' or 'absolute time', and that was a key influence on Einstein when he was developing the general

72

Ernst Mach
Alamy

theory. Mach wrote that '[when] we say that a body preserves unchanged its direction and velocity *in space*, our assertion is nothing more or less than an abbreviated reference to *the entire universe*'.*

Before we look at the link between that idea and the general theory, there's another key point to take on board. There are actually two kinds of mass. One kind comes in to Newton's equation relating force, mass, and acceleration. It is a measure of how much an object resists being pushed about, and it is called inertial mass. The other kind of mass determines how strongly an object is tugged by gravity, and how strongly it tugs on other objects. This is called its gravitational mass. The gravitational force of attraction between two objects is actually proportional to their two gravitational masses multiplied together and divided by the square of the distance between them – Newton's inverse-square law of gravity. The intriguing thing is that for any particular object both masses, gravitational and inertial, are the same. You can measure the gravitational mass of an object by measuring how strongly it is tugged by gravity (simply by weighing it as it is tugged by the Earth) *or* measure its inertial mass by pushing it with a known force to see how quickly it accelerates. These are completely independent tests, and they always give the same answer as each other. Which means there must be some profound link between inertia and gravity. It is also something you see the effect of every

---

* His emphasis.

day – the equivalence of the two masses is the reason why all objects fall at the same rate.

Newton thought that inertia was intrinsic to an object. In an otherwise empty universe, a single sphere would have the same inertia that it has in our Universe. Mach reasoned that inertia is caused by the 'fixed stars' – that is, by the presence of all the other matter in the Universe. Take them away and the lonely globe would have no inertia. This led him to a curious conclusion, involving the equatorial bulge of the rotating Earth.

In everyday language, the equatorial bulge is said to be caused by centrifugal force. All self-respecting physicists hate the term, because there is no such thing. It is a 'fictitious force' caused by circular motion. What is actually happening is that the material at the surface of the Earth near the equator would keep moving in a straight line if it were not being pulled inward by the Earth's gravity. This inward force (a centripetal force) is what stops the planet flying apart, but if someone invented a machine that cancelled out gravity, the machine would not fly outwards like Cavor's spaceship in H.G. Wells' *The First Men in the Moon*, but off on a tangent to the surface of the Earth. If the planet spun fast enough for bits to break off from the equator, that is what would happen to them. The equatorial bulge is best explained in terms of the energy of this motion and the gravitational energy involved, but as I don't want to get sidetracked into those details and I lack self-respect, I will accept centrifugal force as the term to use here.

What matters is that the Earth does bulge at the equator and that this is because it is rotating. Which is where Mach casually tossed a spanner in the works. What matters, he said, is the *relative* rotation. It doesn't matter whether the Earth is rotating and the stars are still, or whether the Earth is still and the stars are rotating around it. Either way, you will get an equatorial bulge. In his words, 'it does not matter if we think of the Earth as turning round on its axis, or at rest while the fixed stars revolve around it'. Einstein seized on this package of ideas, and gave the notion that inertia is a result of the existence of everything in the Universe the name Mach's Principle. But not everyone liked it – it was denounced by both Vladimir Ilyich Ulyanov (aka Lenin) and Bertrand Arthur William Russell.

The principle of equivalence – that gravitational and inertial mass are identical – is one of the cornerstones of the general theory of relativity, and Einstein tried to make Mach's Principle part of the theory. He argued that this identity between gravitational and inertial mass exists because inertial forces are themselves gravitational in origin.

It is easy to make a vague argument in support of this idea (what physicists call, for obvious reasons, a 'hand-waving argument'). Gravity works both ways (actually all ways, which is what is really important). The Earth pulls on me, but I am also pulling on the Earth. The Earth pulls on the Moon, but the Moon is also pulling on the Earth, so both of them are orbiting around their common centre of mass, which lies about 1,700 kilometres below the surface of our planet, not at its centre. If the 'fixed stars' are somehow reaching out with gravitational fingers to influence the motion of an object here on Earth, then there ought to be a corresponding influence from that object which reaches out to the stars. When we try to move something by making it rotate or accelerating it in a straight line, it is moving through the cosmic gravitational web, and disturbing it like a fly struggling in a spider's web. The result should be a disturbance that spreads out through the web and back to the stars (or galaxies, from a more modern perspective), which send back some sort of reaction, like a cosmic handshake, trying to maintain the status quo, resisting the acceleration and producing inertia.

It sounds fine, until you remember that no signals can travel faster than light. If I push the pencil on my desk, it immediately 'knows' that I am pushing it and how much it should resist that push. Signals moving backward and forward through Newtonian empty space will not do the trick. But Einstein's image of spacetime as a flexible four-dimensional fabric in which matter distorts space, and the distortions in space tell material objects how to move, gives us a different perspective, and a way to tackle the puzzle using the equations of the general theory instead of just waving our hands about in a vague way.

When he was searching for a theory of gravity, from the outset Einstein intended that Mach's Principle should be a natural part of the general theory. When people like me describe the behaviour of things like binary neutron stars in terms of dents in spacetime, we ignore the rest of the Universe and pretend the stars are orbiting one another in an entirely flat background spacetime. But the spacetime at any location is in principle affected by the gravity of every material object in the Universe, because there is no limit to the range of gravity. There's a subtle and often overlooked effect at work here as well. If you put a heavy weight like a bowling ball on a stretched elastic sheet like a trampoline, it makes a single dent. Take the ball away and put another one on a different part of the sheet and it makes a different dent. But if you put both balls on together, the pattern of dips that results is not exactly the same as you would get by adding up the two separate dips, because when you add the second ball it is going on to a sheet that has already been distorted by the presence of the first ball. Imagine the complications for the shape of spacetime caused by adding the effects of every material object in the Universe. The shape of the spacetime in which binary neutron stars – or any objects – move is, in spacetime terms, quite literally not a level playing field.

The equations of the general theory of relativity should include the effects of all those distant masses against which accelerations, inertial forces, and rotations are measured. And they do. But there is a twist. Einstein's equations only produce the right Machian influences in one kind of world, the kind in which the Universe is closed. For decades, this was seen by some as a flaw in Einstein's theory, because astronomers thought that the Universe was open, in the sense described in Improbability Three. But the Universe only has to be *just* closed. It can be as near to flat as you like, provided it is on the closed side of the dividing line. The modern idea of inflation and the evidence from studies of the background radiation that the Universe is indistinguishably close to flatness exactly chime with this requirement of the general theory. Rather than being a flaw, the requirement is actually a triumph!

Even better, there is some experimental evidence that the kind of influence on spacetime predicted by the Machian aspects of the general theory are real. Almost as soon as the general theory was published, a couple of theorists used the equations to work out how local concentrations of matter could, in principle, produce a local equivalent of the Machian influence, called frame dragging. In one variation on the theme, you imagine an object placed inside a large, perfectly smooth spherical shell of matter, and the shell is made to rotate relative to the distant galaxies. If Mach's Principle, as incorporated into the general theory of relativity, is correct, the object inside the shell should feel a small force trying to drag it round with the shell. In another version of the idea, the equations tell us that close to a spinning mass like the Earth there should also be a tiny frame-dragging effect. The calculations involving frame dragging were first carried out in 1918, in the framework of the general theory of relativity, by the Austrian physicists Josef Lense and Hans Thirring; but the effects they predicted were so tiny that nobody expected that the Lense–Thirring effect would ever be measured. But, improbably, it was.

In 2004, a satellite known as Gravity Probe B was launched into orbit around the Earth, carrying four gyroscopes in the form of spheres roughly the size of table-tennis balls, each perfectly round to within less than 10 nanometres, meaning there were no irregularities bigger than 40 atoms in height. By monitoring the spin of these gyros the experimenters, from Stanford University, measured a frame-dragging effect of 37.2 ± 7.2 milli-arc-seconds per year, compared with a prediction from the general theory of 39.2 milli-arc-seconds per year. This triumph was only one of Gravity Probe B's achievements, but that's a story for another book. What matters here is that the prediction has proved correct, suggesting that Mach's Principle is right. Before I leave the story of Newton, the Bishop, the Bucket, and the Universe, though, I'd like to mention a prediction that never was made, but could have hinted that Mach's Principle was correct a hundred years ago.

I have been dancing round the terms 'fixed stars' and 'distant galaxies' because until the 1920s what we now think of as the Milky Way galaxy, an island in space containing hundreds of billions of stars, was thought to be the entire Universe. It then emerged that we live in a flattened disc of stars and that there are other, similar islands (some disc-shaped, some not) beyond the Milky Way. Eventually (but not until right at the end of the twentieth century*) it was established that the Milky Way galaxy is almost exactly average-sized, as disc

* See *The Observatory*, Vol. 118, pp. 201–08 (1998).

galaxies go, making it a typical member of its class. We live in an ordinary part of the Universe. By then, it was also well established that there are hundreds of billions of other galaxies in the Universe. Nobody could have predicted that. Or could they?

Although earlier astronomers had studied the band of light across the sky that we call the Milky Way and inferred that we live in a star system shaped like a mill wheel or grindstone, it was only at the end of the second decade of the twentieth century that the American Harlow Shapley was able to put this on a proper scientific footing using what was then the most powerful telescope in the world, the 100-inch reflector on Mount Wilson in California. It would take even bigger and better telescopes to identify other galaxies. But if Shapley had been a Machian maybe he could have inferred their existence.

By 1920, it was clear that the Milky Way galaxy is a flattened disc made up of a myriad of separate stars. Why is it flat? Not because it is a solid object like a grindstone, but because it is rotating. How does it know that it is rotating? Mach's Principle tells us that it is because there must be, far beyond the Milky Way, some distribution of matter which provides a frame of reference against which the rotation of our galaxy is measured. And the natural guess would be that if our Milky Way is an island of stars, the Universe must be filled with other islands of stars – other galaxies. If anybody had made the connection at that time, the work of Edwin Hubble and others which established the existence of other galaxies and the scale of the Universe might have come as less of a surprise, and been seen as confirmation of the accuracy of both Mach's Principle and the general theory of relativity.

It never happened that way, but it is something to think about next time you stir cream into your coffee. As you do so, the coffee rises a little way up the sides of the cup and dips a little in the middle. The improbable possibility is that it does so because it is feeling the influence of hundreds of millions of galaxies hundreds of millions of light years away.

IMPROBABILITY

Simple Laws Make Complicated Things, or Little Things Mean a Lot

The two previous improbabilities dealt with the influence of large things on small things. Hugely energetic events in deep space that produce tiny movements of objects on Earth, and the entire material Universe telling small things how to resist being moved. But tiny things can also have a big influence on the world at large. You may have heard of the 'butterfly effect', a term that is about as misused as the expression 'quantum leap'.* But the improbable truth about the butterfly effect goes much deeper than the popular misconception.

From the time of Isaac Newton until well into the twentieth century, the Universe seemed to be an orderly place obeying simple laws in a deterministic fashion. His famous laws told us how things move when they feel a force, and explained the

---

* A quantum leap is actually the smallest possible change, made in a completely random way. Not quite what advertisers think they mean when they say that a product represents a 'quantum leap' from last year's model.

orbits of the planets and in principle the stars. This led to the analogy of the Universe as like a clockwork mechanism, wound up in the beginning and set inexorably along a predictable path into the future. But almost from the time of Newton himself there was known to be a problem with this image, which was mostly ignored in the hope that it might one day be resolved. It involves gravity and orbits, and it is called the 'three-body problem', although it actually applies to the behaviour of any group of gravitationally interacting objects made up from more than two components.

The problem is that although Newton's laws allow us to calculate with absolute precision the orbits of two objects around one another under the influence of gravity, they do not give exact solutions for problems involving three or more gravitating objects. We can calculate the orbit of the Moon relative to the Earth by ignoring any other objects, and we can calculate the orbit of the Earth around the Sun in the same way, but we cannot calculate the combined behaviour of the Earth–Moon–Sun system,* let alone the rest of the Solar System and the Universe at large. This cannot be done *in principle*, it isn't just that the problem is too hard for us to solve. The relevant equations are said to be non-integrable, or to have no analytical solutions.

We can get round the problem, sometimes, using

---

* The word 'system' is used to refer to any set of interacting objects, such as the Solar System.

approximations. In this example, pretend that the Earth is not moving and calculate how the Moon moves in a short time interval, then ignore the Moon and calculate how far the Earth has moved in that interval under the influence of the Sun and calculate the next step in the Moon's orbit, and so on in a repeating series of steps (iteration). But at each step the Moon is also being influenced by the Sun, and will not be exactly where the previous calculation left it. And what about the Moon's influence on the Sun and Earth? In this example, the mass of the Sun is so much bigger than that of the planets that the approximation works well for determining the orbits of the planets and lesser objects in the Solar System; but if all three objects have about the same mass the problem cannot ever be solved analytically. The key point is that because the equations have no analytical solutions the Universe itself does not 'know' how a three-body system will change as time passes.

This sort of thing would not matter if small errors in the calculation always produced small differences in the final result. But that is not always the case, and that is half of the story of chaos. A system in which small differences in the starting conditions lead to small differences in the later behaviour of the system is said to be linear; but a system in which small differences in starting conditions lead to big differences further down the road is said to be 'sensitive to the initial conditions', and is non-linear. The French mathematician Henri Poincaré summed up the situation as early as 1908 in his book *Science et Méthode*:

A very small cause that escapes our notice determines a considerable effect that we cannot fail to see, and then we say that the effect is due to chance. If we knew exactly the laws of nature and the situation of the universe at the initial moment, we could predict exactly the situation of that same universe at a succeeding moment. But even if it were the case that the natural laws had no longer any secret for us, we could still only know the initial situation *approximately*. If that enabled us to predict the succeeding situation with the *same approximation*, that is all we require, and we should say the phenomenon had been predicted, that it is governed by laws. But it is not always so; it may happen that small differences in the initial conditions produce very great ones in the final phenomena. A small error in the former will produce an enormous error in the latter. Prediction becomes impossible.

A very simple example makes the point. At the top of the Rocky Mountains of North America, there is a watershed, along a line called the continental divide, which marks the geographical boundary between east and west. Rain that falls on the east of the line flows away, eventually, to the Gulf of Mexico or the Atlantic Ocean; rain that falls to the west of the line flows into the Pacific. Right on the line, there must be places where a difference of less than a centimetre in the position where a raindrop falls determines its fate. Two rain-drops falling from the same cloud at the same time may land less than a centimetre apart. One ends up in the Atlantic, the other thousands of miles away in the Pacific. The fate of the raindrop is sensitive to the initial conditions. But there's more. The oceans to east and west seem to attract the raindrops, and the concept of an attractor, linked with ideas about equilibrium, is the other half of the story of chaos.

An equally simple but more homely example of an attractor can be seen by rolling a marble into a round-bottomed mixing bowl. After a few ups and downs, the marble settles at the bottom of the bowl, in equilibrium in a state that corresponds to the minimum energy of that system. This state is an attractor for the system. But there may not be a unique point associated with the attractor. Take the same marble and try to balance it on the top of a pointed sombrero. It will roll off and end up somewhere in the valley made by the upturned brim, but all points around that valley correspond to the same minimum energy state (this is known in the trade as the 'Mexican Hat' potential). The whole valley is a single attractor.

In these simple examples, we are looking at systems that end up in equilibrium, with nothing changing. This is linked to the idea of entropy, which is a measure of the amount of order in a system, with increasing disorder corresponding to increasing entropy. The natural tendency of closed systems – ones which are cut off from the outside world – is for entropy to increase as things get more disordered. In the classic example, if you have a box divided into two halves, one full of gas and the other empty, then remove the partition, gas spreads out to fill the whole box evenly. There is less order, because there is no longer any difference between the two halves of the box. You may have come across the idea of entropy from this kind of example, and learned that systems are attracted to states of maximum entropy. But in the real world, there is no such thing as a completely isolated system. There is always some contact with the outside world, and this changes things significantly.

If two containers are each filled with a mixture of two gases (the classic version of the experiment uses hydrogen and hydrogen sulphide) and joined together by a narrow pipe, there will be a uniform mixture of gases in each container, at the maximum entropy for the system. But if one of the containers is kept at a slightly higher temperature than the other, the lighter molecules (in this case, hydrogen) will concentrate in the hotter container, and the heavier molecules (in this case, hydrogen sulphide) will concentrate in the cooler container. Order has been produced, and entropy has decreased. A very small deviation from equilibrium can completely change the behaviour of a system, and in general a system that is close to equilibrium but not actually in equilibrium will be attracted to a state in which the rate at which entropy is changing is a minimum. Put more simply, interesting things only happen close to equilibrium and when there is a flow of energy through a system. Exactly at equilibrium, nothing changes. Far away from equilibrium, everything changes all the time in a messy fashion – chaos. It is no coincidence that we live on a planet bathed in a flow of energy from the Sun and full of interesting things, including ourselves. Life exists on the *edge* of chaos.

The transition from an ordered system in which nothing significant happens through a state where interesting complications occur and on to a state of chaos can be seen in a real-world example. In a gently flowing river where there is just one rock sticking out above the surface, the water divides around the rock and joins up smoothly on the other side. We can monitor the flow of water by dropping little chips of wood upstream and following them down past the rock. If the flow of water gradually increases, perhaps because of heavy rain upstream, the pattern changes. At first, little whirlpools, or vortices, form just downstream from the rock. They stay in the same place, and chips of wood trapped in them go round and round repeatedly. The vortices are a kind of attractor. But as the flow of water continues to increase, the vortices get detached from the rock, and are carried downstream, holding their shape for a time before they get dissolved into the general flow of the water. New vortices form in their place and are carried off in their turn. But as the flow increases even more, the region behind the rock where vortices form and survive gets smaller and smaller. Eventually, even the water immediately behind the rock becomes choppy and moves in an irregular, chaotic way, and in a really chaotic system there are no attractors. And all this has happened because just one thing has changed – the rate at which the water is flowing. The same system behaves in very different ways if there is a change in just one thing – in terms of the mathematical modelling of a system, a change in just one number. Which brings us to that butterfly and the effect of its flapping wings.

The story goes back to 1959, when Edward Lorenz was working on computer modelling of the atmosphere as a step towards computer weather forecasting. He used the idea that a set of equations describing the state of the weather could be 'run' in a computer to predict the state days or weeks ahead, and he hoped that these equations would show that some weather patterns would be particularly stable, so they would be easy to predict. We would now call these stable states attractors. Of course, the computers he had to work with were far less powerful than those we have today, but he was not actually trying to forecast the weather in the real world, just test how the idea worked on a small scale (what scientists call a 'toy model'). The input to the model was simply a list of numbers, representing things like temperature and pressure, and the output was a corresponding list which could then be turned into a mini 'forecast'.

To his surprise, when Lorenz ran the model twice with what he thought was the same set of input data, he got two wildly different forecasts. It turned out that the difference was caused by a tiny change in the input numbers; the first time he had used six significant figures (for example, 0.506127) and the second time he had as a shortcut simply typed in numbers with three significant figures (in this case, 0.506). The typical difference in each of the numbers from one run to the

This 'butterfly' diagram represents the possible futures of a system
(such as the weather) balanced on the dividing line between
two 'states'. A tiny nudge will send it into one or the other of the
two whirlpools. It is 'sensitive to initial conditions'.
Science Photo Library

next was only one quarter of one tenth of one per cent, but it changed the forecast completely. If the real atmosphere were always as sensitive as this to initial conditions, it would make computer weather forecasting a hopeless task. But it gradually became clear what is going on, and this explains why weather forecasters today are sometimes confident in their forecasts, and sometimes prefer to hedge their bets. The way to picture what is going on is in terms of a kind of imaginary landscape, which physicists call phase space.

Phase space is like a real landscape of a rolling country-side, with hills, valleys, high mountains and deep potholes. Each point on the landscape corresponds to a set of physical properties belonging to the system being investigated. So if we are representing the atmosphere, a single point on the land-scape doesn't simply correspond to a single property such as temperature, but to a particular combination of temperature, pressure and other properties. A mountain peak represents an extremely unlikely state of the atmosphere, while a deep pothole represents a very attractive state. Starting a computer model running corresponds to pouring water on to the land-scape at a particular point. Obeying the equations fed in to the model, the water flows downhill, and is attracted to deep pools. These are the most likely states of the system. But the water may have a choice of paths to follow, like the raindrop falling on top of the Rockies, so where it ends up may be sensi-tive to the initial conditions. A slight shift in the starting point may lead to a big shift in where it ends up. The paths that can be followed in this way are called trajectories, and the points along the trajectory represent the forecast at different times in the future. A typical trajectory in phase space will settle down in one of the pools, circling round and round like the water in vortices formed behind a rock in a flowing river. But if there are two pools separated by a shallow ridge, like a sand bar, the trajectory may occasionally (and unpredictably) cross over and start circling round the other pool. It has flipped from one attractor to another. In the real world, this corresponds to a change in the atmosphere from one state to another.

What meteorologists have found in the decades since Lorenz made his discovery is that sometimes the weather is sensitive to starting conditions and sometimes it is not. These days, meteorologists don't just do one simulation starting with the numbers corresponding to today's weather in an attempt to forecast the weather for days ahead. Instead, they run the same simulation several times with slightly different starting conditions. Sometimes, these runs all give roughly the same answer. The trajectories are all heading into the same pool and circling round in it. But some days the runs give a variety of different answers, as happened to Lorenz in 1959. In that case, accurate forecasting is impossible. Not through any fault of the meteorologists or their models, but because that's the way the world is; the atmosphere at that time is in a state sensitive to initial conditions.

Which is where the butterfly comes in. Lorenz introduced it into the discussion at a meeting in Washington, DC in

1972, where he asked 'Does the Flap of a Butterfly's Wings in Brazil Set off a Tornado in Texas?' Although this is a particularly bad example, because Brazil and Texas are in different hemispheres and weather systems either side of the equator have little influence on each other, his point is that on those occasions when the weather is sensitive to initial conditions, the tiniest change can affect which way the trajectories move through phase space. A better version of the image would be if the weather systems over the tropical North Atlantic were poised on a sandbar in phase space, so that the flap of a butterfly's wings in Senegal produced an influence which tipped it towards one attractor (make a hurricane) or another (do not make a hurricane). But this was never intended as a serious example, and it certainly does not imply that small influences like flapping butterfly wings *force* big systems one way or the other. They simply provide the proverbial last straw.

There is, though, a rather more disturbing version of all this. Some climatologists suggest that among several possible stable states (attractors) for the Earth's overall climate, one corresponds to the conditions we have been used to for the past few thousand years, another corresponds to the ice age that preceded this interval, and a third corresponds to a hot state about 6°C warmer on average than today. The standard computer models of the global warming now happening as a result of the buildup of carbon dioxide in the atmosphere suggest a steady increase in temperature by a little more than 3°C as the amount of carbon dioxide increases to about twice the concentration before the industrial revolution. But Jim Lovelock, the originator of Gaia theory, suggests that a flip into the hot state could occur before the end of the twenty-first century. The analogy would be that the two states are attractors in phase space separated by a small sand bar, and that by increasing the temperature of the globe we are forcing the trajectories to circle higher and higher up the side of one pool, until suddenly they cross over into the other one. If he is right, there is even less time to take action on global warming than most people think.

Leaving those gloomy prognostications aside, however, what can chaos theory tell us about the way the world works? What has happened to the Newtonian clockwork predictability of the Universe?

There's some good news (for us) and some bad news (for the clockwork universe idea). Popular accounts of chaos theory have led to some alarming speculations jumping off from the idea that it means everything is unstable and that because the Solar System is technically in a chaotic state, then as a result of some tiny perturbation like the passage of a comet nearby, the Earth might suddenly switch from its present orbit into another one, or plunge into the Sun. But there are degrees of chaos. That kind of chaos does apply to small objects, like asteroids, under the influence of large objects, like Jupiter and the Sun. But the Earth's orbit is only chaotic within certain limits. Modern computers are able to get round the three-body problem to a large extent using the step-by-step iteration technique, and they have been used to calculate how the orbit of the Earth is likely to change over the next few hundred million years. In the usual way, the calculation is carried out many times with slightly different starting conditions to see if this affects the outcome. The models tell us that there is only a tiny chance of any drastic change in the orbits of the eight main planets of the Solar System over billions of years – essentially, until the Sun dies. But the orbit of the Earth is sensitive to initial conditions in a limited way. In one example, changing the position of the Earth in its orbit at the start of the calculation by 5 metres does not change the final position at the end of the calculation by 5 metres. The 'error' grows until after a simulated 100 million years the model cannot say exactly where in its orbit the Earth is. All the model tells us is that the Earth is somewhere in its orbit around the Sun, which is at least reassuring for us. The whole orbit is an attractor, like the lowest energy trough of the Mexican Hat potential.

You might think, though, that all this is only a problem because we can never say *precisely* where the Earth is in its orbit, or *exactly* what the temperature, pressure and so on are at any particular point in the atmosphere. Surely if we knew these things to enough decimal places the uncertainty would disappear and everything would be predictable, just as Newton thought? And surely in some sense the Universe itself knows where everything is, so it must be deterministic? Surprisingly, the answer is a qualified 'no'.

The problem is that there are not enough decimal places. Even the Greeks knew about the problem, in a slightly different form. It has to do with the nature of numbers. There are three kinds of numbers. Integers – 1, 2, 3 and so on – are easy to understand and work with. Another family can be described in terms of the ratio of two integers, numbers like ½, ¾, and so on. These are called rational numbers (from ratio), and are also fairly easy to manipulate and work with. But the Greeks were well aware of the existence of numbers which cannot be written as ratios in this way, and are called irrational. The most important to them, and the most familiar to us, is pi (π), the ratio of a circle's circumference to its diameter. As a rough approximation, we can use a rational number like $^{22}\!/_7$ in our calculations, but this is *only* an approximation, as we can see if we modernise things by bringing in decimals. Using various calculation techniques, and computerised number crunching, π has been measured to millions of decimal places, and it starts off: 3.14159265358979323846264643383279.

The number $^{22}\!/_7$, a relatively crude approximation, starts off 3.142857, so it is already incorrect by the third decimal place. But the important point about an irrational number in decimal terms is that the pattern of numbers never repeats. The number ⅓, expressed as a decimal, would be 0.333333… with the '3s' going on for ever. But as it repeats, you can specify this as a simple rule, in this case 'keep on writing 3s'. All rational numbers can be expressed by such rules, or algorithms. But to specify π, or any irrational number, precisely, there is no algorithm; you would need an infinite string of numbers, which would require a computer with infinite memory. And this is just for one number – as it happens, a vital number in calculating the orbit of the Earth around the Sun. Even worse, it turns out that most numbers are irrational. This compounds an already insurmountable problem in specifying even the position of a single point on a line precisely. Suppose that the position of that point is $\frac{1}{\pi}$ along the line between two points A and B. You can never express this exactly in mathematical terms. You can express it to as many decimal places as you like, but if the kind of chaos Lorenz discovered is at work, it may be that the next decimal digit, the one you are ignoring, alters whatever it is you are trying to calculate dramatically.

A computer with infinite memory would be required to specify the state of a *single* particle in the Universe. This means that the only system that can simulate the Universe perfectly is – the Universe. Improbably, even if everything is purely deterministic and ticking away like a cosmic clock, there is no way to predict the future precisely, the Universe itself is as ignorant about the future as we are, and for all practical purposes free will exists. Little things really do mean a lot.

All Complex Life on Earth Today is Descended From a Single Cell

There are three kinds of life on Earth, each different from the others at the fundamental level of the cell. The kind we see all around us – trees, people, mushrooms, sea snakes, you name it – is all built up from complex cells which have an inner core, the nucleus, containing the DNA which carries the instructions for life, surrounded by a bag of jelly in which interesting chemistry takes place, all held together inside a cell wall. These are called eukaryotic cells. And all of that complex life is descended from a single cell formed by the merger of two simpler cells a couple of billion years ago.

I told you this once already, in the title of this section. But it is such an improbable suggestion and it is so important that I shall spell it out a third time, for as the Bellman says in Lewis Carroll's *The Hunting of the Snark*: What I tell you three times is true. *All complex life on Earth today, including you and me and a banana, is descended from a single cell*, not in the sense that each of us is descended from a single cell formed at conception, but from one cell formed by a single act of cosmic conception some 2 billion years ago. All plants, all fungi, all animals, all algae – all descended from one single cell. As evolutionary biologists are fond of pointing out, there is no obvious difference between the cell of a mushroom and one of your cells. They both operate in the same way, translating instructions coded in DNA to make proteins and so on, even though the organisms they are part of have completely different lifestyles (unless you have some very peculiar habits).

This discovery is so astonishing that it makes related discoveries that are astonishing in their own right seem almost mundane. But they are not. The first surprise is that there are indeed two other kinds of cell, collectively called prokaryotes, both of which lack the central nucleus that is the hallmark of eukaryotes. But the distinction between these two kinds of single-celled organisms (for that is what they are) did not begin to become clear until the 1970s. Before that time, all prokaryotes were classed as bacteria, although the existence of some unusual species of bacteria was recognised. As techniques for studying the genetic material of cells developed, many of these unusual 'bacteria' were grouped together in a classification scheme and dubbed archaebacteria, because they were thought to be older than bacteria and in some sense their ancestors; but when it was realised that the origins of bacteria go back just as far, the second part of the name was dropped, and they are now known simply as archaea. Which doesn't entirely resolve the confusion, because archaea and bacteria are indeed shown by DNA and RNA analysis to be equally old. Which points to yet another surprise.

The earliest evidence for life on Earth comes from rocks 3.8 billion years old in the south-west of Greenland. These are chemical 'signatures' of life rather than fossils, but by 3.2 billion years ago, life forms in what is now Australia were leaving genuine fossil traces. In round terms, life got started on Earth about four billion years ago, only half a billion years after the planet formed. And it did so *twice*.

So much has become clear as the inner workings of archaea and bacteria have been studied in detail. At the largest scale (for a cell), archaea and bacteria have less than a third of their genes in common. At a more detailed level, the structure of their cell walls is different, and most significantly of all the evidence, the way in which they copy DNA when dividing to make new cells is different. They both use the same genetic code, but they copy it in different ways. These are very profound differences, and to imagine that both kinds of cell could have evolved from a common ancestor 'defies logic', in the words of biochemist Nick Lane. The two forms of life must have arisen separately, but out of the same kind of chemical 'soup', which would explain their similarities. The suggestion made by Lane and others is that this could have happened near hot vents in the sea floor when the Earth was young, with energy from these vents encouraging chemical processes that built up substances as complex as proteins and RNA before cells formed – a flow of energy allowing entropy to 'run backwards', as mentioned earlier. There are other suggestions – I discuss one in my book *Seven Pillars of Science* – and it is likely that we will never know what happened when life got started on planet Earth. We will also never know if the trick actually happened more than twice; there could have been other primordial prokaryotes that have left no descendants today. But we do know that from about 4 billion years ago right up to the present day there have been two separate forms of single-celled life on Earth. This makes both of them extremely successful survivors, but since we are all less familiar with the concept of archaea than bacteria, it is worth spelling out just how successful the former have been.

Typical bacterial cells are between about 0.2 and 2.0 micrometres in diameter, although some are long and thin, and archaea are much the same size. The first archaea to be identified live in extreme environments, such as hot springs and salt lakes, where no other organisms can survive. But they are now known to live almost everywhere, and are particularly common in the oceans, where they make up about a fifth of all microbial cells. The archaea in plankton are among the most abundant organisms on Earth. The versatility of archaea has made them vital in many roles in the environment, including carbon fixation and the nitrogen cycle. They are also part of the 'internal environment' of eukaryotic life forms – the 'microbiota' – and in people they are found in the gut, the mouth, and on our skin, all places where they are involved in many processes which help to keep our bodies ticking over.

Unlike bacteria, however, there are no known archaea which cause disease. Indeed, archaea seem very good at getting along with other forms of life. Many of them are so-called mutualists, which form a mutually beneficial association with other organisms without harming each other, and others are commensals, benefiting from an association either directly or indirectly but neither helping the companion nor doing any harm. The classic example of a mutualist is an archaean called *Methanobrevibacter smithii*, which makes up about 10 per cent of all the prokaryotes in the human gut and interacts with other microbes to aid digestion. They are also found in other species, and as their name suggests, their activity produces methane. Even more significantly, though, the propensity of archaea for mutualism and commensalism suggests something else – why we are here. For more than half the time that life has existed on Earth there were no eukaryotic organisms around to contest the title of most successful form of life on Earth. Then, something happened.

You shouldn't get the idea that life was peaceful until our kind of life came along. Even at the level of single cells, life forms were competing with one another for resources, and mutations were producing new species on which natural selection could operate. Life evolved. And in the competition for resources, one way for a cell to get its metaphorical hands on new supplies was to eat another cell – or possibly for two cells to merge together, pooling their resources. It is now clear that this happened at least once about 2 billion years ago, when an archaean somehow swallowed up a particular kind of bacterium, which retained some sort of independence inside the fused cell, which became the ancestor of all eukaryotes. As with the origin of cells, such events may have occurred more than once; but the similarity of the genetic material of all complex life on Earth today shows that only one such merger produced descendants that have survived.

The story of how this happened was unravelled in reverse, starting with the study of living cells today and working out how they got to be the way they are. It began with the work of the American biologist Lynn Margulis, in the late 1960s. She was particularly interested in mitochondria, which are structures (organelles), shaped rather like grains of rice, that seem to have a semi-independent existence within eukaryotic cells, and which process the energy used by cells. In everyday terms, they take the fuel (or food) coming in to the cell and allow it to combine with oxygen (burn) to release energy (respiration). These components of cells had been discovered at the end of the nineteenth century, and it had been speculated that they were really bacteria which lived in a symbiotic relationship inside the cells. There is a similar situation in plant cells, where organelles known as chloroplasts capture the energy of sunlight and convert it into chemical energy which is used to combine water and carbon dioxide to make organic matter (photosynthesis). It became clear that chloroplasts shared many properties with cyanobacteria, small organisms that live in water, and seemed to have evolved from them.

As techniques for studying DNA developed, these ideas were confirmed by the discovery that mitochondria and chloroplasts have their own DNA, distinct from that of the cells they inhabit. This gave evolutionary biologists an additional tool for investigating the relationships between species, past and present. It turned out that chloroplast DNA is indeed essentially the same as cyanobacterial DNA, while mitochondrial DNA resembles that of a group of bacteria that includes (improbable though it may seem) the one that causes typhus. But these components of cells only possess some of the DNA of their ancestors, not enough to allow them to survive an independent existence outside the environment of the cell, which is largely controlled by genetic material in the nucleus.

Margulis became the leading proponent of the idea that symbiosis was a major force in the evolution of cells, an argument summed up in her book *The Origin of Eukaryotic Cells*. Her enthusiasm led her to suggest a bacterial origin for many of the structures seen inside eukaryotic cells, and the jury is still out on some of these claims. But there is no doubt at all about the origin of chloroplasts and (most importantly for us) mitochondria. They are descended from free-living ancestors that have somehow become incorporated into other cells. The importance of Margulis' work was summed up by Richard Dawkins, who said:*

---

* See *The Third Culture: Beyond the Scientific Revolution*, John Brockman, Simon & Schuster, New York, 1995.

105

Lynn Margulis
Getty Images

> The theory that the eukaryotic cell is a symbiotic union of
> primitive prokaryotic cells ... is one of the great achieve-
> ments of twentieth-century evolutionary biology, and I
> greatly admire her for it.

When Margulis started her work, it was natural for her to assume that this involved mergers between different kinds of bacteria, because the importance of archaea had not been recognised. But it is now clear that the dominant partner in the initial merger was an archaean. Eukaryotic cells derive from a merger between two entirely separate lines of cell evolution.

The leading proponent of this development from Margulis' idea is Nick Lane, who works at University College in London. The essence of his contribution to the debate is the argument that 'the singular origin of complex life might have *depended* on the acquisition of mitochondria. They somehow triggered it.'* This claim is partly based on the fact that although there are a few exceptions to the rule that eukaryotic cells around today possesses mitochondria, the genetic evidence shows that every eukaryotic cell is descended from ancestors with mitochondria. To see why he makes his claim, however, we need to look at exactly what mitochondria do, and how they contribute to the workings of the cell.

....

* See *The Vital Question*, Profile, London, 2015. The ideas Lane describes build from work he carried out with his colleague Bill Martin.

Cells basically run on electricity, but whereas the particles that carry electricity around in the wires in your house are negatively charged electrons, the particles that keep the cell's machinery working are positively charged protons. They are transferred from place to place by chemical processes, and just as the flow of electricity in wires is sometimes likened to the flow of water in a pipe, so the transfer of protons from one place to another is sometimes likened to the action of a pump pushing them along. Mitochondria have a double membrane (an evolutionary development from their own original cell walls), and the inner membrane is ruffled into many folds, which means it has a large surface area packed into a small space. This surface is the key location on which chemistry involving the transfer of protons and the release of energy can take place. The chemical reactions involve an energy-carrying molecule called adenosine triphosphate (ATP), but I don't plan to go into details of the chemistry here. What matters is that one set of reactions stores energy (obtained from food) by pumping protons across the membrane in one direction, and then when the cell needs energy it is produced by letting protons flow back the other way, like water flowing past a mill wheel and making it turn. The combination of these properties means that the mitochondria can supply a lot of energy, anywhere in the cell, whenever it is needed. And (in my opinion equally crucially) they can do so in a steady way. Prokaryotic cells control their energy supply in much the same way, chemically speaking, but all the action takes place near their cell walls, which do not have as complex a structure as mitochondrial membranes, and cannot take the energy where it is needed. In order to use the energy, prokaryotes have to have their genetic material close to the power supply, around the edges of the cell. And because genes are needed to control the workings of the machinery everywhere inside the cell, this can involve having copies of the genes in many places around the rim, which is wasteful of resources.

Cells of complex organisms use a lot of energy. The key process that keeps the cells working – keeps them alive – is the translation of instructions in the genetic code stored in DNA into proteins that do the work of the cell and provide the structure of a body. This uses three-quarters of a typical cell's energy 'budget', whether it is a prokaryote or a eukaryote. The more genes there are, the more complex an organism can be. But the number of genes is limited by the availability of energy. And remember that every time a cell divides and replicates, the entire genome has to be copied to provide a set of instructions for each daughter cell, which also requires energy. In a typical bacterium, there are about 5,000 distinct genes. But in the *smallest* eukaryote there are around 20,000 genes. An average eukaryotic cell has 200,000 more genes than a prokaryotic cell. The difference is entirely due to the availability of energy – thanks to the presence of mitochondria. On the rough and ready assumption that each gene needs the same amount of energy, a eukaryotic cell has 200,000 times more energy available than a prokaryotic cell, and it is delivered wherever, and whenever, the cell needs it.

This brings many benefits. First, it makes it possible for the cell to make extra copies of genes, something which will inevitably happen as more energy is available; we can imagine the copying mechanisms in the first eukaryotes repeatedly going about their work, like the magic brooms carrying buckets of water in the Disney movie *Fantasia*, because there is no way to tell them to stop. This copying is not always perfect, so there will be occasional copying mistakes – mutations – which provide the raw material for new versions of genes, and eventually new genes, to be produced by natural selection. Each extra gene requires more energy, but with mitochondria to hand that is not a problem. The availability of more energy speeds up evolution. Secondly, as the genome no longer has to go to the source of energy, the genes can be packed away at the heart of the cell, in the nucleus, keeping them out of harm's way and leaving space for the cell machinery to do its work. This development must itself have been a result of the evolution encouraged by the availability of energy, but it is unlikely that we will ever know exactly how it happened. Meanwhile, the ancestors of the mitochondria lost the genes that enabled them to survive outside the environment of their host cell, but kept the ones involved in processing energy. They too evolved, to be more efficient providers of that energy. The end product is the eukaryotic cell we know today. But what was the initial 'product'? And how can we be sure that there was indeed only one cell that became the ancestor of all eukaryotic organisms on Earth today?

Lane's argument (which is not accepted by everyone, but looks good to me) is that about 2 billion years ago (long before life moved onto the land) there was a population of archaea living in the ocean and a population of bacteria living alongside them. The two stayed in close proximity because there were mutual benefits, or at least benefits to one side of the relationship. He suggests that one of them may have been feeding off the waste products of the other, but offers this only as a guess. If something like this were going on, the closer the beneficiaries – let's say, bacteria – got to the source of their food – the archaea – the better they would thrive. At some point, at least once, a bacterium snuggled up so close to an archaean that it got inside, and (improbably) wasn't eaten. The invader was tolerated because it did no harm, and it thrived because whatever waste products it needed were available all around it. As it became more dependent on that source, it lost the genes it no longer needed, and became simply a powerhouse.

This is what is sometimes called a 'just so' story, after the book by Rudyard Kipling. It might have happened like that, but the story is really a parable to set us thinking about the possibilities. What matters is that an archaean and a bacterium did get together, and however many times this happened, only one of those unions has left descendants alive today. All distinctly eukaryotic features evolved after this union took place. These features are common to all eukaryotes – even what Lane refers to as 'picoeukaryotes', which are 'tiny but perfectly formed cells ... as small as bacteria yet still featuring a scaled-down nucleus and midget mitochondria'. In all eukaryotic cells, the nucleus is surrounded by a particular kind of double membrane, they all have straight (well, linear) chromosomes (prokaryotes have their genes strung round loops of DNA), they use the same chemical processes to operate the machinery of the cell, and they all reproduce sexually, which plays a major role in evolution.* There is no need to labour the point, since with modern sequencing techniques it is possible to analyse their DNA and see directly how closely related they are. The evidence is compelling. But before I move on, I want to point out an often overlooked feature of the role of mitochondria.

Mitochondria don't just supply energy to the cell. They do so in a controlled way. Which brings me back to the discussion of chaos and complexity. Life exists close to, but not at, equilibrium, feeding off a flow of energy. In the eukaryotic cell, that flow is controlled by mitochondria. If the flow is too slow (like the water flowing smoothly past a rock in a river), we get closer to equilibrium, and nothing interesting happens – biochemistry stops and the cell dies. If the flow is too fast (like a torrent smashing against the rock), we have chaos and the smooth biochemical running of the cell is disrupted. It dies.

....

* See John Gribbin and Jeremy Cherfas, *The Mating Game*, Penguin, London, 2001.

We, along with all eukaryotic organisms, are utterly dependent on mitochondria maintaining the knife-edge balance between two forms of death.

What does all this tell us about the prospects of life existing elsewhere in the Universe? The good news is that if two different forms of cellular life got going on Earth almost as soon as the planet had cooled, the chances of life existing on other planets must be high. The bad news is that if it took 2 billion years before a chance encounter between two prokaryotic cells led to the beginning of eukaryotic life, the chances of such complex life existing on other planets must be very small. And it may be even smaller than it looks at first sight. That chance encounter took place between two different forms of prokaryotic life, where each brought their own distinctive packages of genes to the merger. This immediately gave the first eukaryotes a more complex genome and the raw material for evolutionary processes to operate on. If you need two different kinds of simple cell to merge in order to produce the kind of complex life that eventually led to us, the chances of there being life forms as complex as us on other planets becomes vanishingly small. Even on a cosmic scale, our existence is highly improbable. And even complexity doesn't necessarily imply the evolution of our kind of intelligence. After 2 billion years of eukaryotic evolution, it took an improbable set of circumstances to turn an African tree-ape into *Homo sapiens*.

Ice Age Rhythms and Human Evolution: People of the Ice

The evolution of life on Earth has always been influenced by environmental and climatic changes. One of the most dramatic of these was the event – or series of events – that happened about 65 million years ago and brought an end to the reign of the dinosaurs. This almost certainly involved the impact of a largish meteorite with our planet, although other factors may also have played a part. Since the death of the dinosaurs led to the rise of the mammals, this is a good place to pick up the story of our own origins. But to put this in perspective, 65 million is just over 3 per cent of 2 billion. Eukaryotic life had been evolving for 97 per cent of the time from its origin to ourselves before that meteorite struck.

A variety of geological evidence shows that during the 60 million years or so that followed the death of the dinosaurs, while the mammals were diversifying and filling many ecological niches left vacant by their predecessors, the temperature of the Earth slowly and unevenly declined, as a result of the way the continents were moving around on the surface of the globe, changing the way sunlight was absorbed and reflected, and altering the flow of ocean currents. But by about 4 million years ago a tipping point had been reached.

The evidence suggests that 65 million years ago there were no large ice sheets on Earth, although there may have been seasonal snow on mountain tops. This situation began to change about 13 million years ago, as Antarctica drifted slowly across the South Pole, and ice sheets began to form in what is now East Antarctica. By 10 million years ago, there were small glaciers on the mountains of Alaska. Around 6 million years ago, Australia and South America moved away from Antarctica, leaving a clear passage for a strong ocean current, the circumpolar flow, to surround Antarctica, keeping warmer water at bay and locking the continent into a full ice age. Things were different in the northern hemisphere, where at first warm currents flowed right up to the pole, keeping the Arctic Ocean ice-free. But there, the drifting continents were slowly sliding into the positions we know today, gradually surrounding the polar ocean and drastically reducing the flow of warm currents to the Arctic. In the south, there was a continent permanently covered by ice; but in the north, an ice-covered ocean developed, and there was large-scale glaciation over the land surrounding that ocean by about 3.6 million years ago. The world was plunged into an Ice Epoch, during which ice sheets grew and shrank, but never completely disappeared. The situation that we think of as normal, with ice over both polar regions, is extremely rare, and possibly unique in the long history of the Earth. The fact that we have different kinds of glaciation in each hemisphere is also highly improbable. And the unusual nature of the northern ice cap makes the whole world particularly sensitive to climatic fluctuations that are key as far as human origins are concerned. It is no coincidence that our line developed during the Ice Epoch; but it wasn't cold that was the driving force, it was drought.

An ice age is also a dry age. Water that is locked up in ice sheets would otherwise be in the sea, so when there is more ice on land, the sea level is lower.* Just under 6 million years ago, the ice sheets over Antarctica were several hundred metres higher than they are today, and so much water was locked up in them that sea level fell by about 50 metres (compared with today). This was too low to allow water to flow through the shallows of the Gibraltar Strait, and the Mediterranean dried up; it actually dried up and refilled repeatedly, as the ice sheets fluctuated in size. There was also desert in modern-day Austria. This desertification was linked to the cooling of the globe, because when the world is cooler there is less evaporation of moisture from the oceans, so there is less rainfall. With lower sea levels, the boundary between land and sea was further away from the interiors of continents, so what rain-bearing systems there were had a good chance of dropping

---

* Floating ice has no effect on sea level because it occupies the space of the water it displaces.

their load before they even got to places like Austria. More significantly for the story of human origins, the droughts associated with ice ages also affected the forests of eastern Africa. The temperature there didn't change much as the ice sheets to the north ebbed and flowed; but the rainfall did. I shall go into why the ice sheets ebbed and flowed shortly, but whatever the cause, what matters is that for the past few million years east Africa has been subject to a roughly rhythmic pattern of more and less rainfall – times of feast and times of famine.

I have learned to be cautious about going into too much detail about the specifics of the evolutionary line that leads to ourselves, because new evidence is still being uncovered, and the experts sometimes revise the details of the picture. But the overall picture, based on a combination of fossil evidence and DNA sequencing, does not change. I shall focus on how things evolved from the time when our ancestral line split from the ancestral lines of our nearest relations, the African apes called the gorilla and the chimpanzee.* These are all members of a group, in which we are included, classed as hominids; the term hominoid covers a larger variety of apes including our more distant cousins. In very round numbers, the split that leads to us happened between about 3.5 million and 4 million years ago, with some evidence that the line leading to gorillas split

---

* On any reasonable classification system, we would also be regarded as African apes, but as it was people who made the classification we have been put in a category of our own.

off first, and then the split between ourselves and the chimps occurred. In geological terms, this is intriguingly close to the time when Antarctica drifted over the South Pole and the climate of eastern Africa began to change. Combining evidence from a variety of sources, it is clear that over the next few million years a proto-ape species living in the forests of eastern Africa gave rise to three closely related but distinct ape lines, just at the time the climate was changing significantly. The most plausible speculation is that the evolutionary changes were a response to the environmental changes.

It isn't difficult to see how this could have happened. When the forests get dry, they shrink. This reduces the availability of resources and increases the competition between individuals. It's worth spelling out just what competition means, in evolutionary terms. Individual members of a species are not in competition with other species, but with each other. When lions hunt deer, the lions are competing with each other to catch prey, and the deer are competing with each other to run away. The resulting arms race leads to lions with better hunting skills, and deer with better running skills, as bad hunters starve and slow runners get eaten. In the shrinking forests, individual apes that were better at climbing, say, got more fruit, survived, and produced more offspring than their rivals. But on the edge of the forest, another option was open to the less successful climbers. They got pushed out and had to cope as best they could on the savanna, where those that were better able to cope with the new lifestyle – for example, better at walking upright – did best and left most descendants. This could explain the changes that split us from the other ape lines and made us human.

Exactly which hominid was the direct ancestor of a particular later hominid is not always clear, but the first one to be given the genus name *Homo*, *Homo habilis*, was around in east Africa by about 2.5 million years ago. *Homo habilis* was an ape that walked upright, stood about 1.2 metres tall, and had a slender build but a relatively large head with a brain capacity of 675 cubic centimetres, about half that of our modern species, *Homo sapiens*. By 1.5 million years ago, *Homo erectus* was on the scene – 1.6 metres tall, with a brain size of 925 cubic centimetres. This was the species that spread our ancestral line out of Africa and into Asia. It wasn't until 500,000 years ago that *erectus* had evolved into *Homo sapiens*, the modern human form that eventually spread to every continent on Earth.

But there was more to the environmental changes that accompanied, and probably caused, this evolution than a simple slide down into cooler and drier conditions. Curiously, the geological record shows that over the past few million years the Ice Epoch has been broken up into a repeating pattern in which the ice advances and there is a full ice age for about 100,000 years, then there is a slight warming and the ice retreats into what is called an interglacial state for about 10,000 years. All of human civilisation has developed during the most recent interglacial, but we are still in an Ice Epoch. In eastern Africa, this means that for an interval of 100,000 years or so the forests dry out and times are hard. In the heart of the forest, the successful tree-dwellers are largely unaffected and their lifestyle continues unchanged. But out on the edges of the forest there is a strong evolutionary pressure as many individuals die. The few survivors are increasingly well adapted to the conditions, but may be so reduced in numbers that they are on the edge of being wiped out. Then, there are 10,000 years or so of plenty, and the survivors go forth and multiply. Each turn of the environmental screw ratchets evolution up by another notch.

What survival characteristics will be ratcheted up in this way, in the borderland between forest and savanna? In two words, adaptability and intelligence. And of the two, adaptability is arguably more important. Some animals run faster than us, some swim better, some have more efficient claws and teeth for killing and eating meat, and some have digestive systems better suited than ours to digesting plants. But we do a little bit of everything fairly well – exactly the survival traits needed when resources are scarce and there is fierce competition for them. Intelligence, especially the ability to work out in advance where the next meal is coming from, is the icing on the cake. None of this would have been needed* if there had been no Ice Epoch and there had been plenty of lush forest full of resources. Conversely, if there had been no let-up

---

* By which I mean, there would have been no selection pressure for these traits to evolve.

in the drought, the population of apes driven to the fringes of the forest might have been wiped out before these traits could evolve. It is the peculiar rhythm of the ice ages that has made us human.

This is not just speculation, because we have hard evidence of this pattern of climatic change. The broad picture is revealed by a variety of geological records, spanning millions of years, but the clinching evidence of what has been going on comes from the detailed record of the past million years or so. The details are provided by isotopes of elements such as carbon and oxygen, trapped in bubbles of air in Antarctic ice, or in the form of carbonates in the shells of long-dead creatures in the mud of the sea floor. Cores drilled from the ice or mud contain samples laid down year by year, so going deeper down the core is like looking back in time, and different layers can be dated by a variety of techniques which I have no room to describe here.* The isotopes tell a tale because the proportions of them in the air, and therefore in the bubbles or the shells, depends on temperature. For example, oxygen-18 is heavier than oxygen-16, so water (H_2O) that contains O-18 is harder to evaporate from the sea; and the balance between carbon isotope ratios in the carbonates of deep-sea sediments also tells researchers what the temperature was when those sediments were being formed. Similar effects are used to reveal

---

* See John Imbrie and Katherine Imbrie, *Ice Ages*, Harvard University Press, 1986.

temperatures of the past from ice cores. The results show a complicated pattern of changes over the past couple of million years, but this can be unravelled (another job for power spectrum analysis) to reveal that it is dominated by a mixture of three repeating cycles and some minor components. It is these cycles that cause the pattern of ice ages and interglacials. But the discovery of these rhythms, in the mid-1970s, did not come as a surprise, because this pattern of ice ages had been predicted before there was any geological evidence for it, and before anybody knew anything about the details of human origins.

The prediction developed from work by a Scottish scientist, James Croll, in the nineteenth century; but it was worked out in painstaking detail by the Serbian Milutin Milankovitch, carrying out enormously lengthy calculations literally using pen and paper, mostly while he was a prisoner of war in Hungary during the First World War. The result is sometimes referred to as the astronomical theory of ice ages, but more informally as the Milankovitch Model. It depends entirely on the unusual geography of the globe today, with an ice-covered Arctic Ocean almost completely surrounded by land. Because of this configuration, every winter snow falls on land at high latitudes. At present, during an interglacial, every summer the snow melts. But what would happen if it didn't melt? Snow is white, and highly reflective. By reflecting away the Sun's heat, it would cool the globe, and this happens no matter how thin the snow cover is. In the following winter, which starts off cooler than the one before, more snow falls, both on top of the snow from previous years and further to the south. In a short span of time, geologically speaking, you have an ice sheet which grows upward and outward. There is a positive feedback which will maintain the ice age until something significant changes. None of this can happen over the sea, where the snows of winter melt on contact with water that is warmer than freezing point. The relevant question is not why we have ice ages. Given the present geography of the globe, the natural state of the northern hemisphere is to be in an ice age – Antarctica is permanently ice-covered anyway. The question which needs to be addressed is why we ever have interglacials. Which is where the calculations of Milankovitch and his successors come in.

What matters is not how cold the winters are, but how warm the summers are. An ice age only ends when there is a run of warm summers which melt the edges of the ice back, revealing dark earth which absorbs more solar heat and speeds the melting in another feedback process. The surprise, to non-astronomers, is that the balance of the seasons does change in this way, and it does so because of changes in the orbit of the Earth as it moves around the Sun, and the way it wobbles on its axis as it orbits. This is what Milankovitch spent years calculating by hand, decades before the advent of electric computers.

It will come as no surprise to you to learn that there are three main components to these changes. The longest cycle concerns the orbit itself, which because of the gravitational

Milutin Milankovitch
Science Photo Library

influences of other objects in the Solar System changes from being slightly more elliptical to being more nearly circular and back again roughly every 100,000 years. At present, the orbit is very nearly circular (the eccentricity is close to zero), but a few score thousand years ago it was relatively elongated, with an eccentricity of about 6 per cent. Another effect, called the precession of the equinoxes, results from the way the Earth wobbles like a spinning top. An imaginary line joining the North Pole to the South Pole is not perpendicular to a line joining the centre of the Earth to the centre of the Sun, but is tilted at about 23.4 degrees out of the vertical. It is this tilt, as I mentioned earlier, that gives us the cycle of the seasons; during the part of the Earth's orbit where the North Pole is leaning towards the Sun, it is summer in the north. Six months later, it is winter in the north. And always, of course, it is the opposite in the south. Over a single orbit, the North Pole always 'points' to the same part of the sky (to the same place in the background of stars); but over a cycle roughly 20,000 years long it traces out a slow circle on the sky.

But this isn't all it does. On a longer timescale, roughly 41,000 years, the tilt itself changes, nodding up and down over a range from 24.4 degrees (most tilted) to 21.8 degrees (most upright). The present tilt is roughly halfway between these extremes, and has been decreasing for the past 10,000 years. This means that for the past 10,000 years the contrast between the seasons has been getting less. It is not a coincidence that the most recent ice age ended, and the present interglacial began, when the tilt was more extreme and there was a bigger contrast between the seasons. Although the total heat received from the Sun over a whole year is always the same, what matters is how hot the northern hemisphere summers are, regardless of how cold the winters are.

Crunching all the numbers in modern computers, and including some minor effects, there is a very close match between the calculations of the amount of heat received by the northern hemisphere in summer and the pattern of ice ages and interglacials revealed by the ice cores and deep-sea cores. The astronomical theory of ice ages is correct.

But this is not quite the end of the story. What is it that controls the tilt and wobble of the Earth? The Moon. Without the stabilising influence of the Moon, as I mentioned earlier, the Earth's tilt could vary by as much as 85 degrees. In such a situation, the extreme fluctuations in climate would make it impossible for life forms like us to evolve. It is thanks to the Moon that we have the rhythms of the Milankovitch Model which have made human beings out of forest apes. Which is a suitably improbable note on which to leave you.

FURTHER READING

Easy stuff

Marcia Bartusiak, *Einstein's Unfinished Symphony*, Yale University Press, 2017

John Gribbin, *Deep Simplicity*, Penguin, London, 2005

John Imbrie and Katherine Imbrie, *Ice Ages*, Harvard University Press, 1986

Lawrence Krauss, *A Universe From Nothing*, Free Press, New York, 2012

James Lovelock, *The Revenge of Gaia*, Allen Lane, London, 2006

Not so easy stuff

Nick Lane, *The Vital Question*, Profile, London, 2015

Richard Westfall, *Never at Rest*, Cambridge University Press, 1983

Hard stuff

Charles Misner, Kip Thorne and John Wheeler, *Gravitation*, Princeton University Press, 2017

Thanu Padmanabhan, *After the First Three Minutes*, Cambridge University Press, 1998

Fictional stuff

John Gribbin and Marcus Chown, *Double Planet*, Gollancz, London, 1988

Rudyard Kipling, *Just So Stories*, Wordsworth Children's Classics, London, 1993

NINE MUSINGS ON TIME

*Science Fiction, Science Fact,
and the Truth About Time Travel*

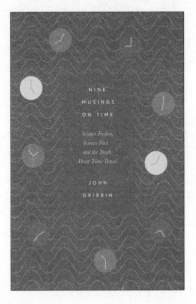

Surprisingly, time travel is not forbidden by the
laws of physics – and John Gribbin argues that if
it is not impossible then it must be possible.

Gribbin brilliantly illustrates the possibilities of time travel by
comparing familiar themes from the science fiction of Robert
Heinlein, Isaac Asimov, Carl Sagan and others with their real-
world scientific counterparts, including Einstein's theories of
relativity, black holes, quantum physics, and the multiverse.

The result is an entertaining guide to some deep mysteries
of the Universe which may leave you wondering whether
time actually passes at all, and if it does, whether we are
moving forwards or backwards. A must-read for science
fiction fans and anyone intrigued by deep science.

ISBN 978-178578-917-5
£10.99

SEVEN PILLARS OF SCIENCE

*The Incredible Lightness of Ice,
and Other Scientific Surprises*

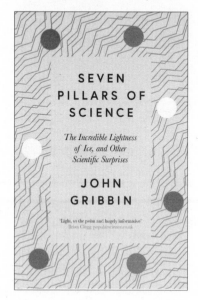

John Gribbin presents a tour of seven fundamental scientific
truths that underpin our very existence.

These 'pillars of science' also defy common sense. For example,
solid things are mostly empty space, so how do they hold
together? There appears to be no special 'life force', so how do
we distinguish living things from inanimate objects? And why
does ice float on water, when most solids don't? You might think
that question hardly needs asking, and yet if ice didn't float, life
on Earth would never have happened.

The answers to all of these questions were sensational in their
day, and some still are. Throughout history, science has been
able to think the unthinkable – and Gribbin brilliantly shows the
surprising secrets on which our understanding of life is based.

ISBN 978-178578-858-1

£8.99

SIX IMPOSSIBLE THINGS

*The 'Quanta of Solace' and
the Mysteries of the Subatomic World*

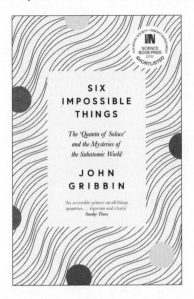

SHORTLISTED FOR THE ROYAL SOCIETY
INSIGHT INVESTMENT SCIENCE BOOK PRIZE 2019

Quantum physics is very strange. For the past hundred years, no one has managed to explain what is really going on in the subatomic world. So physicists have sought 'quanta of solace' in a startling array of interpretations.

Six Impossible Things takes us on a mindbending tour through the 'big six', including the Copenhagen interpretation and the pilot wave and 'many worlds' approaches.

All are crazy, some more crazy than others. But in quantum physics crazy does not necessarily mean wrong. John Gribbin – who has spent a lifetime unravelling complex science – presents a dazzlingly succinct guide to a truly bizarre world.

ISBN 978-178578-734-8

£8.99